FALLING IN LOVE WITH LIFE

*This book is dedicated to
a very great friend
and many other people
who have led me to discover
the untold riches of falling in love with life.*

Catherine McCann

Falling in Love
with Life

AN UNDERSTANDING OF AGEING

the columba press

First edition published in 1996 by
the columba press
93 The Rise, Mount Merrion, Blackrock, Co Dublin

Cover by Bill Bolger
Origination by The Columba Press
Printed in Ireland by
Colour Books Ltd, Dublin

ISBN 1 85607 162 6

Contents

Preface   7

Chapter 1   The Ageing Process   11

Chapter 2   A Sense of Wellbeing   20

Chapter 3   Retirement   42

Chapter 4   Living Positively with Disablements   55

Chapter 5   Managing the Stresses of Older Years   71

Chapter 6   The Satisfaction of the Older Years   85

Chapter 7   Ageing in Wisdom, Hope and Joy   92

Preface

My initial choice of title for this book was 'Successful Ageing'. It was a phrase first coined by a group of researchers into human development in the United States. My second choice was 'Understanding Ageing', with a subtitle 'The way to fulfilled living'. But on further reflection the title that most accurately captures the truth of what I try to say is best summed up as 'Falling in love with life'. This concept is the basic philosophy, a backdrop behind all that is discussed in this book. Ageing is portrayed as a positive process which is all about falling more and more in love with life – with the unique life we have been personally given to live fully to its completion, and to touch and be touched by the vibrancy of life that is all around us.

Falling in love is a reality which happens to us. All we can do to facilitate its occurrence is to put in place certain dispositions and conditions like appropriate attitudes and behaviour. Changing attitudes and altering behaviour, to allow a greater love of life to take root in us, will only come about through growth in understanding.

Understanding is a form of knowledge. It is more than knowing 'about' things, although it can include that. It is a knowing something from the 'inside'; a comprehending, a grasping of a truth which causes us to exclaim: 'Now I see' or 'I now really know what this is about'. Understanding can come in a flash, a moment of truth as we say, but normally it is a process, which over time reveals what is truly real and the deeper meanings that lie behind that reality. Growth in understanding alters the way we perceive things; it changes the way we think and as a consequence the way we feel about things. One of the tragedies of life, according to Anthony de Mello, the Indian mystic, is that there is a shortage of understanding in all of us. He says that often we do not have to do anything to bring about change; it happens, comes about, through the act or process of understanding. Living responsibly is all about living with understanding.

Bernard Lonergan, a modern philosopher, speaks of the centrality of understanding in living: 'Thoroughly understand what it is to understand, and you will understand the broad lines of what there is to be understood.' Understanding is not just about understanding concepts – it is about understanding our own experiences and desires. It is concerned with the search for meaning, which is the essential activity of the human person. This search often becomes more acute as we age. The wonderings of the child reappear, but the questions now emerge from a deeper level, arising out of the accumulation of insights gained through our varying life experiences. We live out of the world of meaning that we have discovered, but there is always more to discover, and so our fundamental attitude of openness or closedness will greatly colour our future. The choice as we age is either to add aliveness to our years or merely to allow years to be added to our lives.

There are many misconceptions, taboos, myths regarding ageing and a way to banish or alleviate these is to try to understand with greater clarity the issues connected to the ageing process. Insight into ageing, when applied to personal living, can enhance enormously the quality of life we live in the present. It also enables us to look ahead more positively at the years that are to come. The secret of living is to live in the present; to live fully each stage of life. Some people have a tendency to live in the future, others in the past, but life can best be lived in the now. Some people's life span may be short, others may live to over a hundred. Quality living, as opposed to a long life without quality, must surely be what is desired. Experiencing a personal sense of aliveness is what this book is about.

I write as someone who is already in her third age, who is an older worker and is preparing for retirement. Having in recent years worked with older people - the fragile older person and their families, preparing fifty-plus age groups for the years ahead, and, most significantly of all, trying really to listen to older people – has led me to read about and reflect seriously on this important period in all our lives.

Some of the information offered in this book is factual. While this provides an opportunity to know more 'about', it is up to the reader to internalise some of this knowledge and apply it to the changes in attitudes and life style that may be necessary to experience life as fulfilling. Growth in knowledge may also come about by allowing ourselves be challenged by some of the possibilities and insights gained from reading this book which may never have been thought about before.

'Falling in love with life' is primarily aimed at those who are fifty or over. When positive and insightful approaches are brought to these and future years, life can be fulfilling, even fascinating. I aim to examine ageing under various aspects and to enable people to understand more clearly what general happenings occur as people age, what pitfalls can be avoided and what things need to be worked at so that we age 'well'.

The first chapter looks at the ageing process in general and the unique phenomena of this century where life expectancy levels have increased enormously. Chapter two focuses on the importance of a sense of wellbeing and concentrates on what individuals can do, in both practical and psychological ways, to contribute to personal wellbeing. Chapter three is on retirement and the importance of preparing for the time when formal work ends. Many fear the possible limitations ageing may bring, so chapter four explores the question of living positively with disablements should these occur. Chapter five discusses the various stresses of the older years and how to manage them, and Chapter six looks at the many satisfactions of this period of life. The final chapter reflects on *wisdom*, the gift *par excellence* of our mature years, and *hope*, that outlook which equips us with the ability to face and live life with optimism and enthusiasm coupled with a sense of realism. The fruits of wisdom and hope are contentment and *joy*.

My overall purpose is to awaken readers to challenge themselves about the great possibilities in life that are there for us in each moment, more than we can dream or imagine. A profound saying supplies an impetus: 'One only grows old when one loses a sense of adventure'. The key adventure is to become more fully ourselves as we move towards the completion of our life span, with the awareness that this is the special contribution we can make to the betterment of humanity. This is all made possible if we empower ourselves and others to grow in insight, hope and realism: insight, that gives us the power to discover deeper meanings in life; hope, that allows us to look ahead with confidence and joy; realism, that keeps us firmly earthed in the wisdom of the present.

CHAPTER ONE

The Ageing Process

We age from the day we are born. Yet when the word ageing is used people assume it refers to the older years. What in fact are the older years? Those who are considered old in one culture, will not be in another. Definitions of the older years will also vary among individuals within a culture. Until recently, many considered the older years to begin at the time of retirement which generally meant sixty-five. However, in Europe, with the retirement age coming down to as low as fifty-five in some places, the question now is, is one old at that age? Most would say no. At what age then does old age begin: seventy or eighty? A light-hearted answer says that an old person is someone who is fifteen years older than we are.

A well known saying is apt: 'We are as old as we feel'. The experience of most people is that they feel young inside even when certain physical limitations are present. It is important that each one, and society in general, fosters keeping alive that 'young inside' person.

Only towards the end of life may a change from this outlook become noticeable. The usual manifestation of this is weariness, at both the physical and psychological levels of the person. Such fatigue often says that a person is now tired of living and is ready to leave this life. This phase may be preceded by a period of frailty when people are and want to be passive. It is a time when they are unable to be other than this way. A false 'enlightened' view of ageing does not always allow for this period in people's lives. Those around can cajole such a person to be and do what they are no longer really able for.

A common way in the western world of looking at ageing is to divide the life span into three ages. These are man-made divisions which are not chronologically or biologically precise but they act as useful concepts. The first age is from birth to around eighteen years. This is a time for development. The second age extends approximately from eighteen to fifty five years. This period is for child rearing and formal work. From the mid-fifties on, when these last two tasks are over, or nearing completion, we enter the third age. The big question then is what is this period of life for? I suggest that it is a time for *fulfilment* – a fulfilment more likely to be achieved through understanding the deeper issues related to ageing.

There are now, as we approach the end of the twentieth century, far more people living in the third age group than ever before. It can be said that this is the first demographically mature society in human history. The advances have been astonishing when we look back.

From the bronze age (around 2,500 BC) until the mid nineteenth century, a period of four and a half thousand years, life expectancy rose from eighteen to thirty-six years. From the mid nineteenth century until now, in other words over just one hundred and fifty years, that figure doubled. At present, life expectancy in the western world is seventy plus years. Many obvious factors have led to this: improved sanitation, hygiene, nutrition, housing, education and discoveries of all kinds, the most recent including the huge modern technological and pharmacological advances. The one great achievement that has caused life expectancy levels to rise has been the dramatic drop in infant mortality. Death in modern society is now largely due to old age. In England, for instance, the same number of people died in 1990 in the 0-60 age group as died in the first year of life in 1909. This does not however mean that individual members of the race are living longer. People in previous ages of history have lived to one hundred or more. The difference now is that more people are surviving into the older years. The number living over sixty-five has trebled this century in the Western world.

Strangely, despite such improvements, a recent Irish report of the Economic and Social Research Institute (ESRI) showed that longevity in Ireland is lower than most other western countries. At present it is seventy-two for men and seventy-five for women. Of those who live to their eighties there are four women to one man. The ESRI's figures also show that those who live to sixty or over manifest no improvement on longevity over the statistics given for 1926. This is puzzling and worrying. What is the cause? The most likely would seem to be unhealthy lifestyles, negative attitudes to the older years, unhelpful expectations, poor preparation; in summary - inadequate understanding.

Other statistics in this ESRI report regarding ageing issues shows Ireland has different demographic characteristics from other European countries. At present figures reveal that 11% of the Irish population are over sixty-five. This is the same figure as it was thirteen years ago, yet in other countries their figures have continued to rise. In thirty years' time in Ireland it will grow to 15%, indicating the rise in the number of older people will be only a modest one. In many countries of Europe it will then be as high as 22%. There are two reasons for these differences. Firstly Ireland's lower number of older people today is due to the high emigration levels in the 1940s and 1950s. These people would have been part of the older age group of today. Secondly, the gradual rise to only 15% is accounted for by the high fertility rate which did not begin to drop until the 1980s. For those who can look ahead to 2030 or longer, due to the recent dramatic drop in fertility rates, the scene will be very changed. The present proportion of young to old will then be completely reversed. The figures for each European country vary slightly due to historical differences.

The fact that so many people are now living into their seventies, eighties and nineties is a great achievement, a great victory for humanity. Unfortunately not everyone sees this as an achievement. Some view it as a great problem.

Problems will undoubtedly exist if nations and individuals do not take cognisance of, and plan for, this reality. Planning will be necessary in many different areas such as pension schemes, health and social care systems, educational programmes that prepare and allow for fulfilled living in these years, years which from now on must be considered the norm for the vast majority of people.

The fact that a greater number of older people survive inevitably makes huge changes in society. It can change consumer power, already noticed in the United States where, for example, advertising and even the arrangement of supermarket shelves are geared more towards older persons' needs. The greater number of frail older people will mean more people leaning on the State's limited resources. The largest increase in numbers of the older population in most European countries is in the eighty-plus age group. Some are fearful that the need for extra resources for the frail older people will happen at the expense of other groups in need such as the various child care services.

Ethical questions such as euthanasia, or its opposite, prolonging life by complicated means with high expenditure involved, are all issues that will come more to the fore. The many complicated and difficult changes that are already occurring need to be faced by politicians now. There is need for governments to provide a suitable environment, in the most general meaning of this word, for people to grow old into. Planners must see that preventive measures are in place for health, social and financial care, as well as providing appropriate and adequate housing, leisure and other facilities. Older people themselves should be included in the formation of all policies related to their needs.

The Commission of the European Communities is beginning to look more closely at many issues related to older people. They have selected five priority areas: the role and potential of the active retired; improving the situation of older women; management of an ageing workforce; transition from work to retirement; care and access to care for dependent older people. Their overall orientation is seeing the concept of the third age as a resource and not as a burden and their aim is to develop this attitude in all member states and to implement this fact in all policies related to older people.

Education is the key factor for everyone. Education of politicians and professionals, as well as the general public, is required so that everyone can face this new situation constructively and optimistically. Education has both a negative and positive role – negative in the sense of eliminating myths regarding ageing, and positive in opening up the possibilities so that fulfilled ageing becomes a reality for the majority of people.

Combating ageism, like sexism and other 'isms', takes time since it involves the rooting out of attitudes, changing of structures and laws, all of which can subtly buttress the continuation of these realities. Attitudes towards ageing develop from various sources but they come particularly from our personal experiences with older people. We tend to be particularly affected by experiences we have had with close older relatives. If that experience was negative it can affect us for the rest of our lives. Research has shown that definite attitudes towards older people, positive or negative, can begin as early as eight years of age. Older people are victimised in many ways by ageist attitudes and they themselves can perpetuate the problem by unknowingly participating and continuing in false roles and behaviours that can colour all aspects of living. Misconceptions include the equating of the older years with sickness. Old age is not a pathological state. People can become ill when old as do other age groups. True, older people tend to have more than one complaint and many of these are likely to be chronic conditions. These can be managed, but the person is not ill because they are left with certain limitation of functioning. Small children cannot carry out all necessary tasks by themselves, hence they are dependent on others, but we do not consider them ill as a result.

Misconceptions also occur around expectations. People sometimes expect older people to have certain antiquated values and ideas and can be surprised when they hear their actual ones, which may be far more progressive than their own. Older people are sometimes expected to do or not do certain things, or to behave according to a preconceived stereotype. For example, many people do not expect older people to be sexually active. This misconception is particularly true among middle-aged children of older parents. Prejudices and negative stereotyping of all kinds need to be challenged. A patient takes on such a challenge when going to the doctor with a painful knee. The doctor remarks: 'What can you expect at your age?', to which the patient replies, 'The other knee is just as old and is quite healthy'!

On the more positive side, education needs to promote personal responsibility for adopting a healthy life style and managing financial affairs realistically. Planning for adequate pension and insurance schemes needs to be introduced early in life and be evaluated throughout the middle years. It is never too early to start working on these issues, but it can be too late, making health and finance major problems in our older years. People sometimes ask what they can do to help older people. The best contribution anyone can make is to care for ourselves in the present and thus prevent or lessen the likelihood of becoming a problem for others when we in turn are old.

A large part of all education is to normalise the ageing process. While we must not deny ageing, neither must we allow it to be a disempowering stage in life. It is essential that healthy attitudes are promoted. The most fundamental attitude is to approach ageing as something we create ourselves, rather than view it as a passively given reality. In other words, we 'make' our own older years to a great extent. It is a time when we need to work at making things happen, as well as allowing for and accepting happenings over which we have no control. Approaching particularly our older old years in a positive manner greatly lessens the possibility of apathy and depression taking hold. Depression can become a major factor for some and this can remain hidden. It is said by some experts that it is a greater problem than dementia. Only 5% of the population over sixty-five suffers from dementia, although that figure does rise with age to 20% for the over eighties. It is still a very small proportion of the older population. We have no say in preventing dementia, but most can help prevent or lessen the effects of depression. Many studies agree that 4% of people over sixty-five have severe depressives disorders and 13% have milder forms. In addition, a further 10% have anxieties and phobias.

There are certain established criteria for ageing well. These include good morale, self-esteem, experiencing satisfaction in our ordinary everyday living, having control over our lives. Erikson, the great American psychoanalyst, speaks of certain features in later life which help to make the above experiences possible. The abilities we need to develop he lists as follows: to be able to adapt to change, to accept the past, to transcend self-preoccupation, and to lose a fear of death. People will come in their own way to degrees of achievement of some or all of these.

- A major ability or quality that everyone needs in life and especially in the older years is adaptability; to be able to adjust to the inevitable biological, psychological, spiritual and social changes that ageing brings. Acceptance of things that cannot be changed is part of this adjustment. Coming to acceptance of what is limiting and undesirable involves discovering meaning in what has taken place. Over time this meaning can deepen.

- The ability to accept our past life includes reconciling how we have actually lived our lives and how we might like to have lived them. Acceptance of mistakes, choices made that are now regretted, helps to contribute to present levels of satisfaction. An inability to do this will detract from an experience of wellbeing.

- Transcendence of self-preoccupation is difficult; it is part of everyone's lifelong fight against selfishness. It is sad to see older people whose lives centre more and more on themselves and their needs, with a gradual decline of interest and awareness of the needs of others. This can happen to people who may have been very caring earlier in life.

- Attitudes towards death have been neglected in many studies of ageing. This could be the result of researchers showing a conscious or unconscious fear or uneasiness about their own mortality, or it could be out of respect for such a sacred moment in life. Fear is an emotion related to the unknown and death is the great unknown for all of us. Some people have a great fear of death. Others face it calmly, and those who work in hospitals would say that this is true of most people. Religion can play a major part in helping people cope with death and dying, yet some, despite their deep faith, can have a great natural fear of death. The actual reality of death grows in people's consciousness from the fifties on when an awareness of our own mortality impinges more into living. This can lead to moroseness, but for those with a healthy realism it can lead to a greater appreciation of the preciousness of life. This in turn results in a determination to try to live as fully as possible each new decade, year, day, as they come along.

There is a theory that many people over their lives develop *efficiency* at the cost of *versatility*. The patterns of thinking and behaviour that we adopt, particularly over the middle years, tend to colour our later lives. A lack of versatility shows itself in an inability to try out new things, take risks, even to enlarge interest and ways of thinking about things. This can result in people being able only to make restrictive choices in their later years when in fact this is a time when creativity is needed. Flexibility and a resourceful spirit are great qualities to bring into the older years. When these are diminished, even small changes can be difficult, like changing personal routines or ways of doing things. If more major changes are deemed necessary, these can become catastrophes.

Developing our potential, and being realistically prepared for what lies ahead, are great assets in dealing with the variety of demands that ageing brings. Part of being prepared is holding in awareness a sense of balance about what the future could hold. The good news is that 80% of older people remain active and independent to the end of their lives. 15% may need help at home and 5% will require institutional care. We are therefore likely to belong to the 80% group. However, we could find ourselves in the other 20% and it is good, at least at times, to allow ourselves to look at this possibility. The benefits of this are twofold. Firstly, it can motivate us to do what we can to prevent such a happening. Secondly, it can make it that bit easier to accept and live positively with this reality should it occur, by the very fact of not being totally unprepared. Examples to call to mind might be: a physical limitation that causes lack of independence even in activities of personal self-care; financial limitation that necessitates giving up an accustomed life-style; the necessity of nursing home care; and, most painful of all, the loss of normal mental functioning through dementia.

One effect of developing our potential is that we become more differentiated or individual as we age, because of the cumulative effect of personal life experiences. A group of teenagers will be much more like each other, due to the lack of variety in their experience. Because of an older person's greater uniqueness it is important that we remain our own kind of person and engage in tasks that have value for us, no matter how strange or eccentric our behaviour may appear to others. Florida Maxwell, an American writer, has these striking words to say about herself: 'Age puzzles me. I thought it was a quiet time. My seventies were interesting and fairly serene but my eighties are passionate. I grow more intense as I age. To my own surprise I burst out with hot conviction'. Our older years call for boldness and imagination. Hence it is important to be wary of telling people how to behave by prescribing how they should live their lives. Widening horizons and encouraging a daring spirit is what needs to be fostered.

Having said that, one thing is definite: the most vital element in ageing well is to keep alive a sense of purpose to life. To have a purpose for our older years in general, and to have a goal or goals for each decade, year, even month ahead, is essential to fulfilled living. In practice this means having a sense of purpose as each new day begins. It means not constantly giving into our inner voice which could say something like, 'Stay on in bed today, the weather is too bad'. Awareness of purpose may grow dim and narrow at times due to illness or stress, but fanning it into flame again and again so that it is personally real in the nitty-gritty of everyday happenings is what gives energy and meaning to living life fully to its completion.

CHAPTER TWO

A Sense of Wellbeing

A sense of wellbeing is an important part of experiencing life as fulfilling. Wellbeing is the result of reasonably met personal needs. We all have physical, intellectual, emotional and spiritual needs which require attention. All four need to be met in a balanced way if a sense of wellbeing is to be achieved. Some people, for example, care well for physical needs but may fall short in some of the other areas. We tend to be pre-occupied with some needs more than others because of personal interests and circumstances. However, it is necessary that thought and time be given to attending to all four areas, which make up what it is to be a fully human person. For example, we cannot become truly integrated if we live solely from the head or at the level of feelings or, alternatively, if we over 'spiritualise' all aspects of living, or become too body-centred. In other words, when there is an over-concentration of energy on one, two or even three areas at the expense of the fourth, wellbeing, fulfilment, an integrated self, will be diminished in some way.

Success depends on taking responsibility for the care of our own physical and mental health. In our earlier years, conscious thought about such matters is likely to have been scanty or spasmodic. From the fifties on, it becomes more important to think through issues related to physical, intellectual, emotional and spiritual wellbeing. This needs to be done, not merely in a reactive way in response to problems that arise, but in a pro-active manner, so that difficulties are prevented or their effects lessened in severity.

Appropriate life styles cannot be imposed on anyone; they are the result of personal choices. These choices are influenced by knowledge and an understanding of the values that make for wellbeing. Some people have the impression that healthy living is a negative concept, where multiple restrictions dominate our lives. On the contrary, a sense of wellbeing is about joy, humour, even exuberance, coupled with the discipline of moderation and knowing how to balance the different areas of living.

Physical wellbeing

Physical wellbeing is greatly influenced by our relationship to our own bodies. Many people have difficulty accepting, let alone liking and appreciating their bodies. Some are often not comfortable with their size, shape, particular features, or certain functional abilities. This can start in adolescence or earlier and is not helped by advertising and a general ethos in society which portrays attractiveness in terms of a certain kind of beauty which is related to youthfulness, slimness, agility, 'good looks'. Yet each human body in its uniqueness is attractive in its own way. We all have a responsibility not to 'spoil' this unnecessarily through unhealthy behaviour or lack of personal care, but to enhance it through adequate and appropriate exercise, rest, diet, and attention to personal appearance.

As people age, the body will consciously claim more attention. It is far easier to give this attention with kindness and care if we are comfortable with, respect and appreciate even our ageing and less efficient body. It is easier to cope with the possible annoyances that certain limitations may bring if we have learnt to befriend our body throughout life.

The following linear diagram illustrates that health and wellbeing are much more than an absence of sickness. The numbers in the diagram do not refer to years, but are figures which indicate levels of wellness. At number fifty on the line, all that can be said is that we have no symptoms of illness. Although this particular section deals with physical wellbeing, mental health levels are also included in this illustration.

Seeing Health as Wellness

0	10	20	30	40	50	60	70	80	90	100
Death	Pneumonia	Bronchitis	Cold	No Symptoms		Energetic Fit		Aware of others		Fully alive
Suicide	Breakdown	Depression	Down			Relaxed	Happy			Creative

Intellectual, emotional and spiritual ageing brings opportunities for maturity for most people. Physically there is some decline. In fact, physically we peak in our early twenties. This is particularly noticeable in certain sports, like gymnastics. From the twenties on, the decline is so gradual as to go largely unnoticed. In fact performance may even appear to increase but this is due to people not realising their full potential in earlier years. In the fifties, certain signs appear, such as odd twinges of stiffness, slight aches and pains, greying of hair and certain sexual changes. These normally do not and need not impinge hugely on our awareness or activity. However, from seventy-five on more noticeable alterations occur. Many of the body's systems and organs work less efficiently, for example, eyes and ears, the heart, lungs, kidneys, joints and muscles. Yet even then, with care and good management, an appropriate level of physical wellbeing can be achieved.

The remainder of this chapter concentrates on areas of physical health over which we do have a say according to the behaviours we adopt. Special problems which arise due to disease or injury, which can occur at any age, but which are more likely to happen in the older years, are dealt with in chapter four. For most people in the second half of life, including those with chronic problems, the following points need to be borne in mind. Common sense, particularly in the area of personal wellbeing, needs to be kept to the fore. To be avoided is an unhealthy pre-occupation with physical health where people verge towards becoming hypochondriacs. There is today a cult of the body that can advocate exaggerated practices – fitness fanaticism, extremes in diets, and exotic beauty-care techniques. Common sense is the best indicator of what is appropriate healthy behaviour to meet the needs of each individual.

Three areas explored in greater detail are:
1. Rest, Exercise, Posture
2. Nutrition
3. Abuses

1. Rest, Exercise, Posture

a) Rest

All our bodily systems need rest, as does our psyche. Rest and sleep are different realities. As we age we need more rest and less sleep. Some people are fortunate in being able to retain their sleep pattern of the average norm, which is around seven hours, into their later years. Others will find their sleep time decreases. Unless it goes below four to five hours it is not normally something that requires medical attention. Sleep itself is a restorative process which the brain needs for both resting and re-organisation. The electrical activity of the brain varies during sleep, showing that there is an active phase where it is thought the brain sorts itself out by shifting information around. There is also the resting phase. Both are necessary. The resting phase of sleep in an older person may not always reach the rem or deep sleep phase, so waking more often during the night becomes more likely. This for many is part of the normal ageing process and need not cause alarm.

Rest, as opposed to sleep, is an absence, or more accurately a minimisation, of physical activity which allows the heart, lungs and other organs, especially the muscles and joints, to relax following a period of exercise. Our exercise tolerance decreases with age and so fatigue levels can rise unless activities are planned to allow for more rest periods in between. Fatigue is a factor which requires some attention. Fatigue can interfere with a number of functions: it lessens physical efficiency during activity, dulls awareness, lowers concentration and can lead to accidents. Getting up late in the morning is not the ideal, unless your normal pattern is to go to bed very late. A rest after lunch is recommended, preferably on top of the bed or on a suitable couch. It is good simply to relax and not sleep at this time, for fear of interfering with night sleep.

Positions of rest require consideration and choice of beds and chairs is important. A good bed needs a firm mattress and to be the correct height for its occupant. There is no ideal chair for everyone, and, as with a bed, it needs to be suited to individual requirements. Unless stiff hips are a problem, you should be able to sit well back in the chair, with both feet on the ground while maintaining a right angle at the hips, knees and ankles - so the height of the chair is very important. The seat of the chair needs to be comfortable but firm and be neither too deep nor too narrow. Ideally, we should not normally sit for longer than one hour at a time.

b) Exercise

The human body is made for movement. Primitive man spent his day largely active, hunting for food. Present western society has become far more sedentary. Many children are brought to school, people are transported to work, buildings have lifts and thus divert from the excellent activity of stair climbing. The supreme example of our sedentary, yet so-called efficient, culture is the TV and other remote control buttons and switches. Some people do try to counteract a sedentary life with weekend activities such as sport and gardening. A better way to ensure a sense of physical wellbeing is to take a reasonable amount of exercise each day.

With ageing the same principle of daily exercise is necessary - only even more care is needed. An appropriate level of agility, strength and stamina must be aimed but not strained at. Little and often becomes more the norm as one ages. There are numerous forms of exercise – the activities of daily living, walking, specific exercises, different types of sport and other leisure activities. All forms are encouraged if suited to your age and health. Joints become stiff, muscles weak and the circulation sluggish from inadequate activity.

Fitness is one of the keys to physical wellbeing. Children, those in their eighties, people in wheel chairs, or those with other limitations, should all aim at a reasonable level of fitness. Fitness has three components. The first of these is flexibility, which means maintaining as full a range of movement as is possible for all joints. Ideally, we should try to put all joints through their full range a few times a week. This is a simple thing to do and need take no longer than five minutes. The second element is strength, which means keeping our muscle tone in good order and this can only be done through exercise. The third factor is stamina. This involves knowing how to pace oneself during an activity, as well as over the sum of the day's activities. If we are unfit, we need to increase our exercise tolerance gradually and the older the person is the more gradual must be the rate of increase. When an individual arrives at a level where they feel comfortably fit, the task then is to maintain that level.

c) Posture

Posture is both a static and a dynamic reality. Our body is always in some particular posture, whether we are in bed, sitting or involved in some activity. In the older years, and particularly with women who are more prone to osteoporosis (softening of bones), the spine can become stooped. Awareness of this fact, plus making the effort to maintain adequate positioning of our body in sitting and lying and during activity, is desirable. Extra care needs to be taken when lifting or carrying objects. We should never attempt to lift more than we are safely able to cope with. Even one mistake could prove disastrous. Particular activities may become possible, for example, by halving loads and making two journeys, or carrying out tasks in stages.

2. Nutrition

Everyone needs a balanced diet. We also need to maintain weight levels that are suited to our size and body structure. Overweight is a real problem for several reasons. It prevents adequate fitness levels being achieved, it puts a strain on the heart and weight-bearing joints, it makes a person a higher risk if surgery is required. Most people do not feel good in themselves when overweight. Research in Ireland has shown that 63% of men are overweight and 48% of women. Other research indicates that if we want to live longer we need to eat less as we age. This is common sense since as activity levels drop, less energy is required. If the food energy, commonly known as calories, are not used up by activity, the surplus is stored as fat in the body.

People can also be too thin for what is normal for them and this also diminishes a sense of wellbeing. It means usually that resistance levels are lower, there is greater susceptibility to infections and disease, as well as insufficiency of energy even for normal activities. Either putting on or losing weight means that clothes no longer fit well, and this makes us feel less good about ourselves. Clothes are, so to speak, an extension of ourselves and as such they can add or subtract from a sense of wellbeing.

The fluid intake of older people, especially those in the eighty-plus years, needs to be watched. There can be a tendency to drink less, particularly if there is a problem of incontinence. Restricting fluid intake is not the way to manage this problem. Approximately eight average cups of liquid a day is considered the norm. Alcohol requires to be taken in moderate amounts as the liver has greater difficulty in metabolising chemical substances. Moderation is needed in all forms of drug taking, including medication. For the older person, medical drugs are usually prescribed in lower dosages.

3. Abuses

Abuses in all areas of behaviour are, as in other age groups, unhelpful, sometimes harmful and most certainly cut across a sense of wellbeing, (other than maybe a very temporary experience of it). There are different categories of abuse: Firstly, taking too much of any food or drink or indulging in harmful addictive substances such as nicotine, alcohol or other drugs; not taking medication as prescribed could be included in this group of abuses; secondly, taking unnecessary risks in activities such as driving, gardening or other hobbies, using poor lifting techniques, constantly adopting poor postures; thirdly, being careless about fatigue levels which can make you more accident prone; fourthly, being lax in regard to the safety of your environment, like ignoring worn, wet, or uneven floor surfaces, leaving trip hazards lying around, inappropriate arrangement of furniture, poor lighting, inadequate heating, goods in everyday use placed on high shelves, bathrooms without the necessary aids such as bath rails and non-slip mats.

Intellectual wellbeing

There is a need to be more consciously aware of intellectual wellbeing as ageing progresses. A big problem for some people as they age is a narrowing of interest, which can result in their world becoming very small. This is both unhealthy and sad when, with some foresight, it could have been prevented.

Except in a minority of persons, the intellect remains intact. Memory may drop somewhat particularly regarding names of people and places. An inability to recall recent events in detail may also be noticed in the older old person. However, the more important powers of the intellect, such as the ability to make judgements, be reflective, have an opinion, learn new knowledge, be creative, remain alive. Reaction time may minimally slow down but most people remain extremely alert, especially if that extra moment is allowed, particularly when taking in new information or trying to work out a problem. Maintaining, and more positively developing, a sense of intellectual alertness can be achieved in many ways and some suggestions are explored here under the headings: Stimulating activities, setting goals, enlarging vision.

1. Stimulating activities

As with our physical self, it is important to 'stretch' our intellect, to include 'mental jerks' in our daily life. There are endless ways of stimulating mental alertness like reading, study, entertainment, conversation. Cross-words, bridge, chess and quiz programmes can be particularly helpful. In Holland and other European countries more older people, including those in their seventies, are going to universities, and maintain above average levels of good health in the holistic meaning of that word. Degree courses of all kinds, using the facilities of the open university, or extra-mural-type courses, are all possibilities open to mature students.

Some people, especially those with a largely functional mentality, query the purpose of continuing education for older people. While one aspect of it may be to skill or re-skill older people so that they can contribute further either in the labour force or in voluntary groups, a main purpose must surely be to educate for fulfilment in the older years. Indeed, education is itself a great enrichment and as such is part of that very fulfilment.

Watching endless TV is undesirable. A survey in England showed that the average number of viewing hours per week for those over sixty-five was thirty-nine hours. It is unlikely that all this time was stimulating. In fact, too much unselected TV watching can have a deadening effect. Such a practice is a habit that can develop out of boredom and a lack of creativity in developing new interests. Interests that have an intellectual component are particularly helpful for intellectual wellbeing. Having the courage to try out new things is desirable, as well as having the ability to try again if these fail. It is very important not to narrow our interests too much to one area no matter how absorbing that might be. For example, if our sole interest is reading and eye-sight fails, the result can be devastating. The same applies to listening to music, if we become deaf. A particular sport or craft may become the sole focus in our life, but if mobility is reduced or hand dexterity is diminished so as to interfere with such activities, we can become very despondent without alternative interests. It is clearly necessary to pursue a reasonably broad range of interests as a preventative measure, variety in itself being an asset that enlarges our capacity to enjoy life in greater fullness. By broadening our interests, conversation with others will be more interesting and as a consequence we will be more companionable and interesting to talk to and be with.

Being creative, possibly unleashing this side of ourselves for the first time, can be a great source of personal enrichment. Doing things for others is also an excellent form of stimulation and more will be said on this in the chapter on retirement.

2. Setting goals

Passivity is one of the enemies of intellectual wellbeing. Keeping our power of choice, ability to make decisions, holding with confidence to our opinions, as well as taking control of our life are all abilities to be held onto as we age. Intellectual energy, which includes thought-out strategies for ourselves, averts the likelihood of moving into a drifting-along type of existence. Effort is required to set goals for the future, be it for the day, the week, the month or even the years ahead. Some people find this comes naturally; others may have to work more consciously at it. I repeat that having a sense of purpose in life is crucial and contributes directly to the level of wellbeing we experience.

3. Enlarging vision

One of the gifts of the older years is having the time to realise, maybe only partially, some of the dreams of earlier years. We can also indulge the opportunity to dream afresh or discover dreams that have lain dormant deep within ourselves. Letting ourselves dream and then gradually giving meaning to that dream by earthing some aspect of it into reality can be personally enriching. It can also surprise us. Important aspects of ourselves lie in our deepest desires, and unearthing this part of us can be liberating. This links well with the words of the poet Robert Frost: 'For I have promises to keep and miles to go before I sleep.'

Keeping in touch with new thinking is helped by keeping abreast of current affairs. Contact with children and youth can also be enlivening and keep us open to the new. A closed mentality limits intellectual wellbeing and can often result in discontent and unhappiness. Constantly trying to enlarge vision, by whatever means, allows for a broadening of our thinking which is always a freeing experience. Coming closer to truth lies at the heart of the journey of life. It is ultimately a combination of stimulation, dreaming, reflecting and creativity that will bring about intellectual fulfilment and this journey or process is unending – there is always more to discover.

Emotional wellbeing

Emotional wellbeing is a complex reality and is difficult to write about since its boundaries are so indefinable. Emotional needs vary greatly throughout life for each individual and often they are the least well met of all our needs. Insufficient attention has been given to understanding emotional health and this even by professionals whose caring work is concerned with the general good of their client or patient. This lack of attention is true for all age groups but it is particularly noticeable among older people who can often be left to their own devices. This could be so because either older persons are expected to know how to cope in this area, or because emotional wellbeing is not considered so important as we get older. Nothing could be further from the truth. Indeed this is a period of life where emotional wellbeing needs to be thought through with extra care since so many negative factors arise. Emotional difficulties vary but key ones are: a reduced sense of self-worth, insecurity, loneliness, sexual diminishment, and losses of varying kinds.

Certain realities that make for wellbeing will be looked at under six headings: keeping alive and developing further our sense of self-worth; maintaining a sense of belonging; learning the art of receiving and giving; learning the art of saying 'goodbye'; working through negative feelings; sexuality.

1. Keeping alive and developing further our sense of self-worth.

Wellbeing is a subjective reality; it is about how we experience life and how we view ourselves. It is concerned with feelings, with what affects us personally. To a large extent our personal experiences flow from the image we have of ourselves. If this tends towards the negative in a consistent way then self-esteem will be low. If this is the case, it is vital that we work at enhancing our sense of self-possession since this is the foundation for feeling good in our deeper self. It is nice and most helpful if others boost our self-worth by affirming it. This however is a bonus factor. The basic affirming of ourselves must come from ourselves. Affirming, believing in oneself as a person of value, is an essential prerequisite to living life to the full. This is so because, while we can dislike things outside of ourselves, if we reject ourselves we reject that which keeps us alive.

In order to change from a position of self-rejection we need to stop making negative judgements about ourselves. It is our thoughts about ourselves that determine our self-esteem. It is the continuing listening to negative thoughts that does damage. Changing our thought patterns alters the way we feel and consequently behave. This is not easy, but it is possible to achieve. Those who have difficulty might benefit from counselling or participating in personal development courses. There is great potential for growth in all periods of life and many in recent years, especially women's groups, have found that this can be fostered through groups whose aim is to develop growth in self-knowledge while at the same time challenging people to look at new possibilities for living. Similar type groups could prove very helpful for older persons.

Our self-image is undoubtedly affected by the attitudes of others, be they from society in general or the significant others in our life. In particular, we can be powerfully influenced by professionals whose services we may seek. All of these categories of persons can enhance or diminish our self-image, although the most powerful force of all is the view we have of ourselves. If this is strong, a person can withstand a great deal of opposition and/or rejection and not be diminished by it. There is also the need not to allow oneself be unduly affected by the many forms of outside influences. The media, school texts, advertising, tend to portray older people in a negative way and this can colour our perceptions. Magazines, for instance, are largely geared towards the young or middle aged which could lead to us saying almost imperceptibly to ourselves, 'we older people are not important, society is not interested in us anymore, they see us as useless'. Even certain literary classics such as the works of Chaucer, Shakespeare, Swift and others often wrote perjoratively about the older years.

Self-esteem can further be coloured by the attitudes we have towards our own ageing. These attitudes will inevitably be connected to the thought patterns we have adopted over time. If these are negative, this one fact alone will profoundly affect our feeling of worth. Self-esteem can also drop if it has been linked too closely with our role in life. If this happens and our formal role has to be relinquished, for example as teacher, manager, homemaker or whatever, then self-worth can plummet. True self-affirmation is based on valuing ourselves for who we are and not for what we do. Valuing our story is part of the self-affirming process. This means accepting the failures of the past and more importantly taking pride in our achievements. In a sense we *are* our story, and consciously 'owning' it at times can be helpful. Connecting with our personal history, with its ups and downs, joys and sorrows is all part of living with fuller awareness. Our goals and desires for the future also flow from all the life experiences that made that story.

2. Maintaining a sense of belonging

Self-worth alone is not sufficient to maintain wellbeing. We are social by nature and so maintaining bonds with people is necessary throughout life. Loneliness, a sense of isolation, can be a problem for some older people. Ideally prevention is the best approach, but if loneliness is present something needs to be done. Our world of relationships can tend to get smaller since losing family and friends through death is more likely. Connections we had with people at work or in other activities also tend to wane. This need not always be; through clubs, associations of all kinds, creating new friendships, the social dimension of life can actually improve.

Whatever situation we find ourselves in, it is important to keep significant relationships alive. Maintaining contact with people through writing, phoning, visiting, being open to receive visitors, are to be encouraged, even if at times this requires effort. Effort may also be needed to maintain healthy dialogue with those we are close to or live with. As in other periods of life, relationships can become stale, or alternatively they can flourish into having a new lease of life. Relationships, especially valued ones, need to be worked at all through life.

A sense of belonging can flourish if there is a strong sense of connectedness to a group and this could include the larger groups in society such as nation, church, the world community. Even a hermit requires to have a keen sense of belonging. Indeed, a more profound one is necessary to sustain him or her in the solitary life.

Linked with this sense of belonging is the need of celebration. The celebratory side of life is important at all stages of life, and it is difficult, if not impossible, to celebrate on our own. Various happenings, events in life, call for celebration. A lack of 'play', lightheartedness, rejoicing with others, tends to make life dull and monotonous. We need the relief, the excuse at times, to break from our normal routine. A capacity for enjoyment plays an important part in a fulfilled life and celebrations are a delight-filled way to keep this side of life alive. Those blest with a sense of humour are particularly fortunate.

3. Learning the art of receiving and giving

Both of these 'art' forms require thought, practice and fresh approaches as we age.

a) Receiving

It is true that most people find it easier to give than to receive. Some people, and especially those who have a great need to be needed by others, find it particularly difficult to receive, whether it is a compliment, a gift, a gesture or a service. The ability to receive graciously is an art, which has the value of benefiting both giver and receiver. The true receiver is open to accept what is offered (assuming it is appropriate to do so) in a spirit of gratitude, being grateful for both the act itself and the concern shown behind it. Acceptance also involves humility. The proud person can receive, but they are liable to see the gift as something that enhances their status. The humble person accepts in a way that enhances the giver. Humility and simplicity in the receiver is more likely to make the giver feel good and this can have the effect of enlarging the giver's spirit of generosity even further.

As we age, it is likely that there will be some tasks that we may need help to accomplish. The more intimate the task, the more difficult it can be to receive help. However, if the art has been practised in easier things, then when the more difficult situations arise there will be a greater facility to accept the necessary help.

b) Giving

An essential element in achieving fulfilment in life is to retain always the ability to give to others. Due to the possible limitations that the older years may bring, be it of purse, physical mobility or for other reasons, more creative ways of giving need to be developed. The basic giving is the giving of respect to the person or people we are with, being aware of their needs as well as our own. As energy levels fall, there can be the temptation to excuse ourselves, and shirk our responsibility to go on giving. If this does occur, we ourselves suffer. Our world will become smaller and more self-centred and this in turn makes us less interesting to be with. In the older years the form of giving is likely to change, shifting more to the area of thoughtfulness and less to that of activity. There are still endless ways to give: being as present as possible to others when they are with us; listening with attentiveness; remembering things of importance in the lives of others; showing a concerned interest in their world; lovingly challenging a person when that seems the compassionate thing to do; giving a smile; thanks-giving - all are genuine and valuable forms of giving that are open to everyone.

4. Learning the art of saying 'goodbye'

One of the keys to fulfilled living is developing an ability to cope with loss. Loss comes to us in many ways and includes people, places, pets, activities, personal functional abilities, dreams. When reality shows us that certain things are no longer possible for us, it is desirable to move towards acceptance of this fact and not to live in the unreal world of false hopes. Saying goodbye means letting go of what is lost and moving on to living fully within the present situation as it really is.

The necessity of saying goodbye to people who have died is obvious and this is achieved by going through the process of grieving. Other losses, especially the major ones like broken relationships, deep disappointments, personal inability to carry out favoured or even essential tasks, leaving our home, also call for grieving. Loss of anything major usually affects several areas of life and so time is required to adjust to the altered situation. This could mean months or possibly a year or more, depending on how severely the loss affects an individual. The secret of fulfilled living for everyone is to work towards acceptance of both major and minor losses. This can only be done by going through the painful process of grieving.

It is our reaction to incidents such as loss that causes us the upset we feel. Reaction to loss is likely to move through the recognised phases of denial of the loss to begin with, and then bargaining can occur. This can be with oneself, others or God. This period is often followed by anger and despair, until finally a person moves to the beginning of acceptance. This process is not a neat one and people tend to move backwards and forwards through the various phases. When some level of acceptance is arrived at, then we are able to shift our energy from constantly fighting the pain of the loss to concentrating on what is possible in the new situation that follows the loss. At this point, fuller living begins again.

Saying goodbye is also about letting go of all the 'could-have-beens', and realising the positive dimensions of the present. Those who make this transition can discover that life becomes fulfilling again, maybe even more fulfilling. Since loss is concerned with parting it is always painful. The only way forward to finding meaning and joy in life again is to work through the pain. Leaving a hobby we have enjoyed for years, letting go of long held ideas about things or ways of doing things, giving up independence regarding certain activities, are all difficult realities which may need to be faced. It is precisely by meeting the challenge, letting go of what was treasured, and moving to the altered situation with hope and an exploring spirit that sets out to discover what is positive in the new, that quality living will begin again. Ideally, this process is best worked through with the support of other people.

5. Working through negative feelings

The challenge and necessity of working through negative feelings is life-long. In the older years the source of such feelings is likely to come in three ways. Firstly, there is the unfinished business of the past. Secondly, there are the fears and anxieties connected with the future. Thirdly, there are one's reactions to the unpleasant happenings of present reality.

As we age, incidents of the present, or personal reflection on life in general, may release negative feelings connected with our past life. Some of these we may never have been faced, or maybe were swept under the carpet. Others could have been so deeply buried as not even to emerge into consciousness up to this. Past hurts, deep resentments, disappointments, bitterness, unresolved anger, may surface. Such feelings can be triggered in quite unexpected ways. If these feelings are not faced and attempts made to work through them, they can remain a cloud, an irritant, that will cut across our sense of wellbeing and possibly lead to depression. Excessive anxieties and fears regarding the future can also take an unhealthy hold on us. A sense of realism, an anchoring of our life in the present is the way to cope with such feelings. The future is unreal, and the fears envisaged may never come about.

Talking over our anxieties and fears, as well as the negative feelings connected with the past, with a trusted person can be helpful. If such feelings persist, professional help may be necessary. This should not be considered a luxury. Admitting to such a reality and taking appropriate action shows strength. People seek attention for physical ailments; emotional ailments can be just as much, if not more, crippling.

There may also be need for self-forgiveness. Difficult as it may be to forgive others, forgiving ourselves can be even harder. Looking back over our life, there are likely to be some regrets, either for deed or omission. We can regret certain things we said or did which we would prefer we had not said or done. We can regret also the things we could have done or said, but did not do or say. Holding onto such regrets or failures as we may now perceive them is undesirable. Learning from them, making amends if this is possible and considered appropriate, and moving into the 'now' of life is what is necessary for emotional good health.

6. Sexuality

Wellbeing is closely linked with sexuality. A sense of aliveness flows from a person being comfortable and in tune with their femininity or masculinity. Being aware of our sexual self is an important part of fulfilled living in the older years. If the sexual side of ourselves is let atrophy, part of what lies deepest in us is no longer able to give us life. The spark, or more aptly the sparkle of living, is no longer alight and as a result living can become drab.

Sexuality is intimately connected with our sense of worth as a man or woman. All relationships are coloured by the feelings we have about our attractiveness or lack of it. Society today in this regard favours older men, in the sense that they are often seen as distinguished when the grey hairs and wrinkles appear. Women, partially due to commercial pressures, often try to do all they can through colours and creams to hide such signs. There is nothing wrong with this, as long as the focus is not solely on physical appearance. Real attractiveness comes from within, from an alive personality that values and expresses one's womanhood or manhood.

As we enter our older years, we may need to consider what sex means to us. Our sexual life, as with other aspects of living, changes over the years. The sex drive for men is less intense than it was in earlier years. We cannot recapture the type of sexual satisfaction of youth or middle years later on in life, but that does not mean it is no longer important. Sexual satisfaction is now different. It can be extremely fulfilling if it is kept to the fore as an important part of personal living. While it can and does include sexual intercourse for partners into their seventies or even later, it does mean for many couples opening up, and maybe discovering for the first time, the deep pleasurable experiences that can be found in a broad range of activities. There are many ways of making love, of giving and receiving sensual pleasure that results in deep emotional satisfaction.

'Pleasuring' is a term sometimes used regarding sexual fulfilment and by this is meant any sexual experience that makes us feel good. Small gestures of tenderness such as stroking, hugging, kissing, even a look or a smile, can all convey sexual meaning for people. Genital intercourse can be extremely satisfying if time is allowed for relaxation and intimate fore play and if both persons are sensitive to the particular needs of the other. Many are ignorant about what to expect regarding their own sexuality and that of their partner. Sexual interest, performance, needs, alter and for sexual life to continue to be fulfilling it is necessary to be aware of the changes in both oneself and our partner. Sharing openly with each other about such changes helps greatly in coming to a mutual understanding of what modifications in practice and behaviour are needed. It would appear from research that some couples deprive themselves of practically all forms of sexual expression due to an inability to work through this period of sexual adjustment.

Men in particular appear to find the transition difficult when their level of performance alters in their later middle years. Some fail to realise that such changes do not abolish their sexual powers. Fears of becoming 'impotent' at this stage are more likely to result from psychological impotency than physiological incapacity. An erection takes longer to develop and will not be experienced with the same level of intensity, but it can last longer than with a younger man. Ejaculation may or may not occur. Women, especially if they stay healthy, can remain sexually active for the whole of life. In fact, many women become more sexually active and less inhibited after the menopause, and the sexual interest of older women can remain very alive. Women alter less than men physiologically and the basic changes depend on the level of sex steroids available. One of the most noticeable changes is a reduction in vaginal lubrication (which is something that can be helped by the use of a cream or jelly).

The major shift that is necessary to achieve sexual satisfaction in the older years is one of orientation – the realisation that it is the giving and receiving of mutual affection and pleasure that is the important reality. How this is achieved is secondary. The affirmation that comes from being intimately loved by someone, and being able to reciprocate with our own love of the other, brings healing, growth, comfort and pleasure. The enjoyment and sustaining aspect of a deep sexual life in the older years is one of its great enrichments. Many say they have discovered that their sex life has become 'even better' in later life.

Sexuality is important also for those who are single, including those who now find themselves widows or widowers. Many widowers marry again, widows less frequently. The option of

settling down in a new partnership is a possibility to be kept
open for all who find themselves single. There are those who
have opted to remain single for life, such as religious and others.
But for all, no matter what our life circumstances or choices,
keeping alive a sense of our own masculinity or femininity is a
very important part of ageing 'well'. Remaining life-giving to others, whether in the context of partnerships or friendships, calls for
an alive sexuality. Denying this side of ourselves, or letting it
peter out so to speak, harms health and prevents full living.

Spiritual wellbeing

It may seem strange to some that this section on spiritual wellbeing follows immediately on that on sexuality. But in fact these
two realities are closely related. Both are linked with what is
deepest and most intimate in ourselves. Spiritual wellbeing is
rarely adverted to or thought about. Even the phrase itself could
sound unfamiliar. Spirituality is concerned with realities such as
truth, beauty and freedom. It also includes a religious dimension. People can confuse spirituality with religion; the former is
a broader concept and includes the latter. Spiritual values tend
to hold a more prominent place in our lives as we age, and one
of the ways of enhancing spiritual wellbeing is the degree of
openness of mind and heart that we bring to our older years.
Some people appear to shrivel as they age, whereas others let
their spirit self become ever more expansive as the years go by.

The search for truth, for meaning, is present in everyone. It is
about looking for answers while, at the same time, being able to
live with the questions which tend, as life goes on, to multiply
and outweigh the answers. Discoveries emerge from the continued search if carried out with honesty and a sense of realism.
Such discoveries can lead to a more satisfying explanation of
life's great questions as we try to probe, even enter these great
mysteries. At the same time, trying to find answers to specific
issues may prove ever more difficult. In a strange way life becomes more complex and yet more simple, and a holding together of these two opposites is one of the fruits of the wisdom
of the older years. The more truth is discovered, the more it is
searched for, since the very discovery has a power which leaves

us unable to stop searching for deeper truth. Finding truth has a compelling quality which draws us ever further into what it is that has been found. Truth changes our lives more than anything else. There are layers of meaning to human existence and exploring the truth of the real, especially as it touches us personally, is the way to gain insight into what it is to be truly human. Florida Maxwell, writing about ageing when in her eighties, says: 'A long life makes me feel nearer the truth, it is a time of discovery. "Of what?" I am asked. We must each find out for ourselves, otherwise it won't be a discovery.'

A reflective person, with an enquiring spirituality, can pursue a growing desire to explore truth about the deeper meaning of life, with an openness which is enlivening. Such a spirituality can break through prejudices, narrowness, assumptions, that were held sacrosanct for years. This can lead to an exhilarating sense of inner liberation. The truth sets us free. True spirituality is the way to enlarge the life of the human spirit, which if not challenged can atrophy into a life of apathy and diminishment.

The capacity both to create and enjoy beauty can become keener and more delight-filled in our older years. The ability to appreciate beauty in fresh and new ways, unknown until now, is one of the great possibilities and is open to all. The enjoyment and awareness of beauty will be further developed in the chapter on 'The satisfactions of the older years.'

Breaking into greater degrees of inner freedom is one of the greatest gifts that ageing can bring. Freedom is about perspective, where we no longer cling to, or are tied down by inessentials. It follows from answering the call to conversion, in this instance the conversion of perspective. This conversion process leaves the human heart and mind free to soar, no longer being bound by previous restrictions that we are now able to let go.

Religious faith can become very important to people as they age, even if this side of life was on the fringe or even discarded for many years. A growing religious sense, more accurately termed the religious dimension of human experience, can come about through the growing realisation of our own mortality, and this can have a calming as well as a challenging effect. Just as an experience of deep suffering can open us to the reality of a power greater than ourselves, so too a deeper consciousness of the reality of our own death can have a similar effect. The power greater than oneself will for many be God. Specific religions will articulate faith in God with certain differences, but the life of the mystics, those who live life most deeply of all, shows us that a simplicity emerges which can soften the edges of differences between the great world religions. Wisdom – intellectual, emotional, but especially spiritual wisdom – is what emerges in those who are open to care for their sense of spiritual wellbeing. Spirituality is a profound part of what lies deepest in us and more will be said about it in the final chapter.

CHAPTER 3

Retirement

Retirement is a strange term and is not really apt to describe the period of life it refers to. The word itself speaks of a movement away from something but gives no indication of where that movement is going. It is this lack of direction that makes the term unhelpful. It clearly shows it is an end of something, but it is less obvious that it is about the beginning of something else.

Retirement for most people is a major life event. In many cases it involves a transition from one status in society to a status which is less clear and which often has an 'ex' note about it. For instance, we speak of an ex-teacher, ex-nurse, ex-postman. It insinuates a withdrawal into a roleless life. As a result, retirement can be viewed in a negative and narrow way and as a reality that is uninviting. For most people it is understood as that period in life when formal paid work ends.

Yet this view is somewhat narrow. It excludes many women, homemakers, whose work of childrearing is also over – do they never retire? It also raises questions regarding the future view of retirement. With patterns of working arrangements changing, it is difficult to predict what retirement will mean in the twenty-first century. The present norm of permanent pensionable jobs is unlikely to continue. High rates of unemployment will also affect the ethos of the older years in ways that are difficult to foresee.

The present situation for most people is that a definite change takes place when the responsibility of child-rearing and work comes to a close. This change may be a painful one for some; for others it is something warmly welcomed. It is more likely to be difficult for those men and women who have been workaholics, those who have experienced their self-worth as attached to their role, and parents who find it hard to let go of their children as they grow to adulthood. Those who look forward to retirement are likely to be people who have a broad view of life, have a range of interests, and can look ahead with pleasure to their older years as a time of opportunity.

Retirement, or preferably, the period of the Third Age, has certain characteristics. Life is liable to be less formally structured. The structures that do exist are those chosen by ourselves. Some people find the transition from a very ordered existence a relief, whereas others are uncomfortable when they have to move out of a regular timetable that they have been accustomed to for years. Alan Omstead, an American journalist, wrote an insightful diary following his retirement. He discovered that nothing out there really depended on him. Nothing was imposed, there was nothing he really had to do. He spoke of the cancer-like idea which tempts and says 'so do nothing'. He said a deliberate act of will was needed to escape such thoughts and that, without externally-imposed demands on time, there is need for self-imposed demands. He saw clearly that most activities make a difference for oneself. He also makes the interesting remark that self-imposed routines create the possibility for leisure: 'They are the bread and butter of the leisure sandwich. Leisure, freedom from obligations, can only exist in relation to obligations.'

People often look forward to retirement, to engaging more fully in various projects and activities they did not previously have time for. Yet when they actually retire they never get down to doing what they intended to do. Some find they have time on their hands and yet do not have the will, or discipline, to make these aspirations a reality in their lives. The early retirement years in particular have a lot to do with making things happen rather than just letting them happen.

Retirement alters many areas in our lives, for example, relationships, financial status, health, the use of time, responsibilities. The changes that occur intimately affect the way we experience life for the remainder of our years. For some this can be an empowering happening, for others disempowering. It can be disempowering if an individual experiences herself as: 'I am who I was'. It is up to each one of us to choose. Consequent on this basic choice are the multiple choices open to us when we are retired. The range of options is so varied that some find that very fact stressful. Surveys show that our ability and willingness to exercise choice depends on a number of factors, such as education, health, social status and self-esteem. It is a time for relinquishing the many 'shoulds' and 'oughts' that we previously found ourselves tied by. Part of the transition in retirement is discovering that this is mainly a time for what we want to do, and is not about what we feel we should or ought to be doing.

Happily, the days of the poorhouse are now over and, with improved benefits for the older person provided by the state, many of today's older people find themselves in a more secure financial state than previous generations. Apart from pension schemes, there are numerous benefits, allowances and treatment opportunities older people can avail of according to income. There is no longer, either, the constant worry and financial demands of the middle years when bringing up a family could have resulted in severe restrictions on income and freedom.

The pre-retirement period

Our later years at work, or as worker in the home, may have become a time where excitement and enthusiasm had waned. Coming up to retirement can provide an opportunity to work through this barrier where life might be beginning to appear meaningless, and to discover through increased understanding that a new and fuller life is possible when our normal work comes to an end. The experiences of older workers differ. For some, the last few years can be difficult and this could easily colour in a negative way their approach to retirement. One reason for this is that at present there is an over-valuation of younger workers and an under-valuation of both the productive capacity and experience of the older worker's contribution. Some people even experience unfair discrimination against them. Employers have to balance possible diminishing competitiveness with the advantages of the valued experience that many older workers have to offer. The problem of feeling under-valued can lead to a pessimistic spirit developing. Fears of illness and dependency, as well as despondency when looking in a mirror at our changing physical appearance – all of this can have a psychological impact which is unhelpful and can lead to a real experience of feeling diminished as a person. Others may have had good experiences in their last decade at work or at home. Such people are likely to have remained on 'top' at what they were doing. Alternatively, some may consciously decide to gradually 'wind down' within their existing full-time work, by, for example, not taking on extra responsibilities. Consciously doing this, while remaining very much alive in ourselves, allows part of our energy to be geared towards looking ahead at future possibilities and even trying out certain activities in small ways in non-working hours.

There are in fact today many more varied routes into retirement, so that the boundaries between full work and complete retirement are becoming blurred. The transition to retirement, in other words, is more flexible, some taking early retirement and others continuing on after sixty-five. For the majority, the flexibility that does exist is mainly concerned with exit, few having the option to stay on past the retirement age even on a part-time basis. In Ireland retirement has been influenced by early retirement schemes, voluntary redundancies and improved pension arrangements. The self-employed and some who work in the private sector are more likely to have alternative options of easing themselves into retirement. Up to the 1980s the main reason for taking early retirement or part-time work was ill-health. Now it is more labour-market related. There is, too, a shift emerging in attitudes to work and leisure. Growth of leisure and ongoing education pursuits are seen as important values in life, important enough to entice some people from work at an earlier rather than a later stage. The timing and meaning of retirement are not always open to personal choice, but, regardless of the when and the how, it is good to realise that our pleasant or unpleasant anticipation of the retirement years affects not only retirement itself but also quality of life in the period preceding it.

Preparing for retirement

Understanding ageing and the many issues related to it is the best overall way to prepare for retirement. Some people avoid all preparation because it would seem they do not want to think about it. This group mainly comprises those whose chief interest in life has been their work. Statistics in England have shown that an above average number of such people, most of them men, die soon after retirement.

Retirement is just as important a stage in life as previous ones. Possibly it is more so, since it can comprise a third of life. It needs to be perceived not merely as a period of 'not working' but a time of great possibilities, including that of continuing to be a contributor to society. It provides an opportunity to make a fresh start – a start which flows from the wealth of our previous life experiences. It turns out for some that they were never as busy as they are now since retiring. Such people experience retirement as giving a new lease of life. For those who do not move through the work to retirement phase of life, namely the unemployed and others, there is a greater danger of drifting into the older years. Such people are denied the 'fresh start' opportunity which retirement offers. Thought, planning, and educational programmes to prepare for the older years are, it could be argued forcibly, just as important for such people.

Preparation for retirement calls for reflection on the meaning of the years that lie ahead and on the particular activities best suited to realising that meaning. This process of reflection prevents us sliding into apathy, to a way of life where existing rather than full living becomes the norm. There is so much potential in all of us that we have never used. We all have talents and insights which were under-utilised or were not utilised at all. Our older years provide the opportunity to redress this. Courage, an ability to take risks, knowing how to manage failure in a positive way, are all helpful attributes that enable us to launch into the deep of new adventures.

While working on attitudes and approaches towards retirement is the basic preparation, looking at practical issues is also very necessary. Most people would do this in a personal way, but some form of help can prove beneficial. Some employers offer pre-retirement courses and, if one of these is not available, being adequately informed on financial matters, including entitlements, legal, health, safety and other issues, can prove valuable. The challenge, too, of being opened to the range of facilities and opportunities available, some of which were likely to have been previously unknown, can also be beneficial. The words of the fool to the king in Shakespeare's *King Lear* are apt: 'We should not grow older before we grow wiser.' Preparation is all about seeking the necessary wisdom before embarking on retirement. This helps us avoid unnecessary pitfalls and, more positively, opens us to a wealth of opportunities.

Addressing financial issues needs further elucidation since it is such an essential part of preparing for retirement. In fact, this preparation should start early on in life. Adequate financial security in the older years relieves a basic worry about income and makes for our latter years being comfortable and pleasing. Finance is also necessary to embark on some of the activities and pursuits that have already been mentioned. Indeed money is required for many leisure activities. The level of optimism we have when viewing our future is often linked to our level of financial security. Financial fears are common and can be real or imagined. Income in the third age comes from four sources – state pensions, occupational pensions, savings or part-time work. Those who are fortunate may have two or more of these sources to draw on. However, a reduction in income is certain for most people when they retire. This may lead to the need to adjust our life-style. Someone who is unprepared to face the reality of what a drop in income entails is likely to fare less well than the person who has thought through such implications. Professional help may be necessary if the income drop is severe. Unnecessary fears can make us tight with money, leading to an inability to enjoy a lifestyle that is affordable.

The present system of pensions and social welfare payments needs much thought. A team of authors from the World Bank wrote a report entitled 'Averting the old age crisis'. They point out the responsibility of each person to ensure economic security in their older years. They stress that both developed and developing countries need to reform their old age security systems in order to cope with the huge increase in numbers of the older population. They recommend that the ideal system would be a combination of pay-as-you-go plans, privately managed plans, and personal saving and annuity plans. People will need to start saving younger, which some will find difficult even if they have the money to do so. Looking ahead to the older years is not seen as a priority for twenty- and thirty-year-olds, or even for those in their forties.

A unique phenomenon in Ireland is the number of people who own their own houses – 75% as compared with 45% in other European countries. (The number rises to 80% for those over fifty-five.) While this is desirable in many respects, it does leave people with less fluid assets available in their older years. This is a factor which calls for consideration both by individuals and the State. The question to be faced is, is home ownership the best way to sustain quality living in our older years, or would alternatives be more desirable?

The retirement years

Retirement can be a a fruitful and enjoyable time. It is also a time to avoid certain problems. This section examines a range of possibilities and problems related to this time of life under five headings: relationships and roles; leisure; education and personal development; creativity; volunteering.

1. Relationships/Roles

A major change such as retirement affects the whole of life and particularly our relationships and roles. A key sustaining factor throughout life is healthy relationships, and the alteration that retirement brings can have beneficial or adverse effects. Awareness of this is enormously important for fulfilment in the older years. The more crucial relationships are examined below, particularly in relation to possible problem areas.

a) Partnership relationships

Many flourish in new ways in the older years; others run into difficulties. A common scenario is the following. A husband or partner's main focus in life up to retirement has been his job or career, and he has devoted much of his energy and interest in this direction, with little quality time being left for his family life. He postpones the notion of family satisfaction to his later years. When the time arrives, he discovers that he has missed moments which can never be recaptured and may have to grapple with the realisation that his children have grown away from him both physically and psychologically. His wife, due to the absence of her husband at work, and also the absence of quality presence when he is around, has made a life of her own, where her interests and needs are met by friendships and activities in which he is not involved. In other words, both partners have grown apart from each other. It will take time and work for a satisfying relationship to develop again, especially in the altered situation where children are likely to be no longer around. His wife, too, may resent her husband coming back to the household full-time, intruding in what has over the years become more and more 'her domain'. His retirement can mean an intrusion in the lifestyle she has developed for herself. Tensions will almost inevitably surface between the couple and feelings such as resentment and disillusionment are likely to emerge. With children no longer the focus of their main shared interest, it takes much give and take, understanding of where the other partner has come from, and determination, to work afresh at their couple relationship. Coming unstuck from patterns of living that have emerged over time is never easy, but it is imperative that an effort be made by both if a fulfilled existence together for the remainder of their years is the desired aim. The reverse situation can also be true. If the wife has been the main breadwinner, or if the husband retires before his wife and he in turn has developed a satisfying life for himself during those years, he too could find his way of life interrupted when his wife retires. Whichever way it goes, sensitive adjustment that allows for individual freedom and togetherness, held in some form of balance that is acceptable to both, has to be worked out. Many discover that this is a completely new period in their life as a partnership.

b) Children, sibling, friendship, community relationships

All of these sets of relationships can grow or be put under strain at the time of retirement. This is particularly the case when such persons live together in the same house. Adjustment is called for on both sides. Each one needs to allow the other freedom and to be able to alter expectations when necessary. Generosity and an avoidance of demanding behaviour are called for by both or all parties. In the early transition days, when patterns of future behaviour are being laid down, extra care needs to be taken.

One particular type of situation that can arise is when older parents move in to live with one of their children. The advisability of such a move requires much discernment. In some instances it works well; in other cases it can prove disastrous to the point where an entire dysfunctional family situation develops. Openness and much dialogue are essential prerequisites before such a step is taken. Part of the discernment process is to look at the range of alternatives and to seek outside help if necessary in coming to a decision.

Honesty is also needed on inheritance issues. Children can subtly or directly show an assumed right to claim their parent's wealth, be it property, the family home, or capital. Parents may need to exercise their right to hold onto what is theirs for their own quality living and not be persuaded to feel badly doing this unless there are very good reasons to the contrary. If, for example, nursing home care is deemed best then the family home may need to be used as the source of income to provide this type of care.

Making a will should be done early in life when assets begin to accrue. Numerous family rows and splits can occur when this is not done. It is particularly important for single people and non-marital partnerships, especially those with children, to make wills, since rights of inheritance in such situations are likely to be less clear.

c) Grandchildren

Relationships with grandchildren and the question of the grand-parenting role can take on great significance following retirement. This is an important but sensitive area that requires delicate handling. Grandchildren and great-grandchildren can be one of the delights of the older years, provided healthy relationships are established between grandparents, children and grandchildren. There are pitfalls. For example, children ask their parents (usually their mother) to look after their children, both to give her an occupation following retirement and to allow themselves to continue working with greater ease. Such a situation can start off as beneficial to all concerned but can go awry unless constant re-evaluation is allowed for. Grandparent(s) can take on the role willingly to start with, but may later find the demands and the energy drain too high. They may also come to feel taken for granted by their children and begin to resent being so tied down. Possibly early on or later in their grandchildren-minding role, they realise other opportunities are being lost, that there other avenues in life they would like to have followed and maybe now it is too late to do so. They may have realised this early on but felt uncomfortable about going back on the commitment they gave to their child. If only one grandparent is involved, it could be a source of tension between the grandparents or it could cut across the grandparents having more time together for rebuilding afresh their own relationship. The actual minding of children's children can be fraught, when ideologies and standards about child-rearing differ between grandparents and parents. Some grandparents may be seen as too indulgent, others as too strict. Finding the balance that is helpful and does not confuse the grandchild is particularly necessary. Having pointed out some pitfalls, there is need to re-emphasise that healthy fostering of relationships between grandparents and grandchildren can be a source of great delight and be of enormous benefit to both parties.

2. Leisure

Leisure is something distinct from work, and is also something different from free time. Free time is sometimes termed 'non-obligated' time, when seen in relation to work. Leisure is a particular use of non-obligated time. The importance of personal choice is vital as to what activity an individual selects. The number of leisure pursuits is endless and, obviously, what is leisure for one

may not be for another. The essential note in leisure is that it is
something we enjoy. A leisure pursuit has the added dimension
of having some discipline attached. For instance, if swimming is
chosen as a leisure pursuit then we go regularly, even on the
odd day when we do not particularly feel like doing so. If some
discipline is not present, whatever the pursuit is, the activity is
likely to peter out over a relatively short period of time. A real
problem that happens to some people is that they have had, or
made opportunity for, little leisure time during their working
life and so are poorly prepared to make good use of their free
time when retired.

Leisure activities include all forms of sport, such as golf, bowl-
ing, walking, outings, social gatherings, card games and entertainment of all kinds. More private forms would be reading, listening to music or other hobbies. An interesting EU statistic
shows that Irish people spend more in general on 'fun' than
their European counterparts. Ireland spends 12.1% as compared
to 8.7% in other countries. It certainly is to be desired that these
figures would apply equally among older people.

What prevents some people from participating in outside-the-
home leisure pursuits is lack of adequate transport, as well as of
suitable premises and facilities. This particularly applies to people with disablements. Providers of all forms of leisure activities
need to take greater account of the problems of some older people.

3. Education and personal development

Intellectual activities have been discussed in chapter 2 under intellectual well-being. The same chapter also makes reference to
the value of continued personal development work.

4. Creativity

The linear diagram in chapter 2 showed that one of the great
signs of vitality in life is creativity. The middle years for many
have been a functional period of life, where working to build a
home, raise a family and attend to work are uppermost values,
and to these most personal energy was directed. The third age is,

as suggested, a time for fulfilment. It is a time par excellence for unleashing the creative self which may have been stunted to the point where individuals say they have no creativity. This is never true. The way we do things, the very gestures we make with our face, hands, body, are all creative actions. One of the great joys of retirement is to enlarge the creative part of us that lies deep within. It may be discovered in specific art forms such as painting, sculpture, poetry, drama, dance, writing, crafts, or it may disclose itself in more hidden ways of thought, ways of relating to others or the world, meditation, or prayer. Creativity can come through the appreciation of many art forms as well as participating in the art itself. More will be explored on this topic in the chapter on the satisfactions of the older years.

5. Volunteering/Service to others

Discovering a meaningful role in society after retirement is often achieved through some form of voluntary work. Such volunteering can be of a formal or informal nature. The former normally entails joining an organisation, club or society. The range of possibilities available is vast; for example, they could be connected with politics, the arts, sport, religion, social issues. Active retirement organisations, most of them being geographically based, can open up people to a great variety of activities and projects within their own locality. Helping out at local churches or clubs are examples of less formal voluntary work. Informal volunteering, or acts of service of all kinds, is something people opt for as individuals. A few people may join together on some project and form a small informal group.

An essential note to quality living is to know that we are still contributing to society, to know that we are givers as well as a receivers in our relationships with others. The actual level of contribution may be small, but if it is meaningful that is what makes the difference. Volunteering, or acts of service, enhance self-worth and contribute a great deal to the realisation that life is worthwhile. To be able to go on giving to people, or to projects that benefit others, keeps alive a sense of purpose to living. Skills, talents, insights and the other riches developed over life can be beneficial to others, often in unexpected ways and unusu-

al circumstances. Having confidence in the value of our contribution is also helpful for ourselves. The mutuality of the help
that is given and the help that is received can assist in restoring a
present imbalance where the 'wisdom of the expert' is seen to
outshine the 'wisdom of the years'. Both forms of wisdom call
for respect and both in their own way have something special to
contribute to enriching the lives of others.

CHAPTER 4

Living Positively
with Disablements

Disablement is used here as an umbrella word to include diseases, disabilities, or disorders. All of these cause some form of interference in one or more of the following areas: normal body functioning, mental ability, behaviour. While the older years must not be equated with disablement, the reality is that some older people will be so affected. Trying to categorise disablements is difficult because the range of problems is so broad. *Diseases* can be acute or chronic, congenital or terminal. *Disability*, normally the result of some chronic condition, can encompass a variety of problems such as restriction of movement, impaired vision or hearing, altered function of a body system, or mental deterioration. *Disorder*, a term usually used in reference to behaviour, is a consequence of things like alcohol or drug abuse, or mental disturbances such as anxieties or phobias.

An older person is liable to all forms of illness just like people of other age groups. Particular diseases become more prevalent – coronary heart disease, stroke, arthritis, cancer, diabetes, Parkinson's, blood pressure problems, cataract, Alzheimer's and other forms of dementia. Anyone with a previous chronic problem such as a respiratory condition, arthritis or schizophrenia, will inevitably have to contend with that as well as other problems that may arise. As we move into the seventy-five-plus age group, there is greater likelihood of having more than one condition to cope with as well as becoming more accident-prone and generally experiencing the frailty of this period of life.

Having stated some brief facts about disablement in the older years, the main focus in this chapter is on reactions, attitudes and management of disease, disability or disorder.

Reactions

1.Illness is a crisis-provoking event

An ESRI survey showed with great clarity that people's main problem in the older years was not loneliness, or lack of finance, but the fear of illness and dependency. Undoubtedly, the transition from full health to ill health, be it acute, chronic or terminal, is a crisis-provoking event. For most of us, the diagnosis of an illness constitutes a crisis unless the illness is minor and of a transient nature. Hearing a major diagnosis pronounced on ourselves is an event that can have greater significance than some of life's other major crises such as a loss of a spouse, retirement, relationship difficulties, children leaving home. The severity of the illness, one would assume, is the measure of the level of crisis. In fact, it is largely our subjective reaction, rather than the objective nature of the illness, that determines the degree of upset. The personal loss of morale that can occur pre-disposes a person to adopting an inappropriate and unhealthy life-style. Such a life-style is often drifted into and lacks the element of challenge. Over time this adds further to low morale. Health personnel and services need to give more attention to the morale effect of illness, to facilitating its improvement, seeing this as an important part of their contribution to the recovery process. On the whole, there has been a lack of emphasis on developing coping mechanisms to help patients manage their condition constructively. The professional focus has been on trying to cure, to the detriment of time spent trying to enable patients to manage their own problems, guided by the knowledge and expertise which the professional freely shares. The overall 'treatment package' should include the giving of information about the nature and prognosis of the illness, as well as supplying ongoing education on the physical and psychological management of this unique person, with their specific problem, in their particular life situation.

2. Receiving a diagnosis

Receiving a diagnosis is a jolt to our body and mind – to our whole person. It can cut across a particular functional ability which most of us would have previously taken for granted. But it affects more than mere function; the whole of life – dreams, plans, relationships, the ability to do what we want to do – are all likely to be affected in some way. An illness is sometimes experienced as a sentence, because at the heart of the experience are the acute feelings aroused by the thoughts of freedom being curtailed.

The moment of diagnosis provokes shock. If the disease manifests itself in an acute and serious form, it will give rise to profound uncertainty and confusion. Those who have been waiting months or longer to discover what is wrong may have suffered a great deal of anticipatory anxiety which can also lead to doubt and confusion. When the diagnosis is finally pronounced, such a person's immediate reaction may be one of relief: 'Now at last I know what is wrong'. In such cases, the shock reaction is likely to be delayed until the reality of what is now finalised sinks in. When the shock stage subsides, negative feelings are likely to emerge as the implications of what has happened begin to dawn. Intense anger and/or sadness are common feelings. Bargaining can take place – with self, others, God. What is happening is that the person is going through the process of grieving for the loss or losses that are most keenly felt as a result of the illness. This is natural and in a sense healthy. Over time, however, it is desirable that the person comes to complete the grieving process and arrives at some level of acceptance of what has happened. Some, alas, remain unaccepting of their situation, while others move to partial, or, best of all, full acceptance. Acceptance, partial or full, allows us to live again within whatever limitation has taken place. The amount of support and insightful help that is available over this period will play a major role in facilitating the person to come to terms with what has taken place.

3. The acceptance journey

On the journey towards acceptance, it may at first be difficult to see any positives in life. This is acceptable in the early stage of grieving, but it is imperative to turn away from this negative position, which also serves to hinder recovery. Non-acceptance of what has happened usually includes an inability to face the prognosis in a realistic manner because pessimism clouds vision. Continuing to fight emotionally against the diagnosis and prognosis absorbs energy and makes fulfilled living impossible. From such people it is not uncommon to hear two particular phrases: 'If only ...' or 'When I am better', both revealing an outlook that is not rooted in reality. The 'if only' remark indicates distorted aspirations that are not earthed or connected to the truth of the present situation. This wishful thinking prevents a person looking at and experiencing the positive aspects, and there are always some present no matter how black things seem. 'When I am better' connects with the future which is always something unreal. Such a comment masks the truth. Often we know the truth deep down when we allow ourselves to be honest with ourselves. Gradually, there is need to face gently the challenge of what getting better means. It is a relative concept. People close to such a person can be unhelpful if they collude in the game of pretending that the person will recover according to their false desires, when they know better. Not telling the full truth is allowable and sometimes desirable, but pretence is unhelpful and hinders positive living. We are not obliged to speak 'the whole truth' in most circumstances in life, but this is very different from denying truth, from not facing what is real in a given situation. If the 'if only', 'when I am better' syndrome persists, professional help, especially in the form of counselling, may be needed. Facing truth does not destroy hope, as some people think. Genuine hope springs from being rooted in the truth of the present. It does not operate from pretence or falsehood.

4. Different situations/Varied reactions

Reaction to an illness is rarely a once-off thing. There are ongoing reactions as the path of the disease alters. Different diseases take different courses. Some are progressive, causing symptoms which constantly manifest deterioration, the rate and degree depending on the condition in a particular person. Some are more constant, in that after the initial episode and the adjustment period, there then follows a time of stability. Other conditions are characterised by periods of relapse, with often unpredictable times of feeling well and relatively symptom-free, followed by the opposite.

Some diseases have a life-threatening dimension. However the good news is that, with advances in early detection and constant improvement in treatments, many of these conditions, including cancer, can be managed, even cured. Despite this fact, the reality is that most people diagnosed with a potential life-threatening illness, live (as do their families) with some uncertainty. Such uncertainty is realistic, but a sense of realism also requires that fears be kept in perspective and in the background, especially as individuals get on with positively living their lives again as the months move to years and then to further years.

There are also some people whose reactions can be overly positive, in the sense that they become unrealistically optimistic about themselves in a way that is unhelpful, and maybe even harmful. Understanding is the way to finding a true and healthy balance which allows for realistic living that is neither over-optimistic or pessimistic.

While reaction to chronic illness has been our main focus, the process is not dissimilar for those who are diagnosed with terminal disease. Due to the likely shortening-of-life element in such an event, the shock will inevitably be greater. However the process of coming to terms with, and moving to living life as fully as possible in the now, is probably even more important precisely because of the likelihood of a shortened life-span. Part of the coming to terms includes, in the acute forms of terminal illness, coping with any 'unfinished business'. Such business could be practical, emotional or spiritual. Completing this, at least partially, is often what enables a person to live fully the days, months or longer that are left to live.

Acute illness forces us into the present. When one is very ill, personal energy is largely spent on existing in the now of pain, uncertainty and the general feeling of being unwell. Fears of the future, of death, may intrude, but the basic want is to be able to hold on until one gets through the acute stage of illness.

Attitudes

1. Taking responsibility for personal attitudes

It would be nice for all of us if we could live without physical or psychological trauma all our lives. This of course happens to no one, yet there is a common assumption that it is not right when unpleasant things affect us personally. A reaction 'it's not fair', can in turn arouse the dangerous emotion of self-pity, which exclaims 'poor me' or 'why me?'. While this reaction is understandable in the early days following a crisis, it is undesirable to remain in this mood for longer than is necessary. This depends on how seriously we take responsibility for our emotional states. If the 'poor me' attitude persists, it can result in the person knowingly or unknowingly taking refuge in the martyr role. This approach is unhelpful and may even be destructive. It makes life miserable for ourselves and also those who are close to us.

2. The search for meaning

Ultimately our reaction to unpleasant happenings comes from our basic philosophy and spirituality. By spirituality is meant that part of us that gives personal meaning to ourselves, to all that happens to us whether it comes from within ourselves or from without. Grappling to find meaning is necessary, particularly during crisis times. It is desirable to try to discover meaning when a serious illness is diagnosed, or even when minor changes take place in health which cause us to believe that the beginning of a downward slide to greater ill health and dependency has commenced.

3. Changing personal attitudes

It is through the search for meaning and perspective that attitudes are born. They are formed over life, but we can change them if we are honest about facing truth and alter our perspectives accordingly. Understanding, insight, is the way to bring about that change. Part of the understanding referred to here is the realisation that moments of crisis, while initially negative, contain also within them the possibility for personal growth. In other words, there is a positive dynamic inherent in everything, even in those realities that cause us physical or psychological pain. We can 'go to pieces' in crisis, or we can grow enormously, even to unleashing a potential in ourselves that we were unlikely to discover otherwise. Thus the crisis of disablement provides the possibility for either challenge and growth or for disaster and despair. The event itself is not what decides which of these it will be; rather it is our attitude to what has happened, the way we perceive it, which dictates the orientation we adopt. It is not an either/or situation; many people's attitudes fluctuate along a continuum between the two poles of negative and positive. The important thing is to be able to shift attitudes, at least into the positive half (see diagram). The more positive attitudes become, the more likely fuller living will be experienced and this can take place in the midst of severe illness, be it acute, chronic or terminal.

Attitudes to illness

-	+

| Disaster | Challenge |
| Despair | Growth |

If we have been positive about our ageing process, and if we are comfortable with our body, the trauma of illness is likely to be accepted more easily and with a greater sense of perspective. It will not be seen as 'the end of the world', as the end of the A-Z of life, but simply as the end of XYZ. Genuinely facing up to and grieving for the loss of XYZ, and then letting go of the loss, or abilities that are no longer available, allows us to move on to concentrate on and enjoy the A-W aspects of life that remain. Some so bemoan the section they have lost that they are unable to see, let alone enjoy, what they still have. A prerequisite for allowing this move in attitudes to take place is to have previously kept alive, and preferably even enlarged, our range of interests so that while following an incident of illness certain interests have to be forgone, there are already alternatives in place. Unless, as we age, we have created for ourselves interesting things to focus on, a particular disablement is more likely to take hold of us in a way that preoccupies us and thus becomes more crippling than need be.

4. Disorders

The focus in this chapter so far has been illness and disability. Disorders can also cause problems. With the mellowing of time, it is possible to look afresh at certain addictive behaviours such as smoking and drinking. It is never too late to give these up or limit their use; to be avoided is increased consumption. Two factors can act as potent motivators: an attitude-shift which desires quality living in the older years, and an awareness of the possibility of an illness being worsened by continuing with such behaviour. The attitude: 'Well, the harm is done, there is no point in changing now' is not based on factual evidence. Any reduction is worthwhile, since it is beneficial to health and well-being.

Management

1. An overview of managing disablements

Healthy attitudes form the basis of managing disablement. Good or bad management in turn influences attitudes. Management is about how best to cope with a particular disablement. It also includes how we manage our total life situation in relation to an ailment. While diseases, disabilities or disorders have common manifestations which make each one identifiable, there are enormous variations within a particular condition. No two people have exactly the same symptoms or problems following a stroke, arthritis or whatever. What differentiates one person from another with a similar complaint is both the specific presentation of the illness in this particular person and their reaction, attitudes and ability to manage the problems that arise.

2. The on-going nature of managing disablements

Management is practical – it is the 'how to' which enables us to cope with living. It allows us to maximise the use of existing abilities and to develop new ones. It also helps to prevent deterioration where possible. If deterioration does occur, then learning to cope with this changed reality is all part of management. Management is never something static. There is a constant ebb and flow with many illnesses – the acute and chronic stages, the flare-ups and remissions. Added to this is the possibility of multiple pathologies occurring. For instance, someone has a stroke and after time has learnt to accept and manage this difficulty. Then suddenly a cardiac problem arises. The effort to work a second time through the arduous journey from shock to acceptance may at first seem too much. However, the only alternative route is one which brings diminishment and is a form of opting out of life. The acceptance road is never easy, but there is no shortcut. Allowing the necessary time to make this journey has to be done since there is no instant method. Illness is a blow which can shake confidence. Regaining confidence in ourselves and in our ability to do things requires patience. It is helped greatly by the encouragement and support of others.

3. Some particular situations which require skilful and sensitive management

Obviously, with confusional conditions, the many and often distressing problems will have to be managed by others – a partner, sibling, children or outside agency. Increasing numbers of people with intellectual disability are now surviving into old age. (Formerly such a disability was termed mental handicap.) Their needs require specialised care, but this is not part of the scope of this book which is aimed at older people who are mentally capable of managing their own older years. What are pertinent are the difficult problems brought to older parents who still have children dependent on them as a result of mental or physical handicap. If one or both parents' levels of disablement increase, there is need to manage this stressful situation with delicacy and realism. Painful decisions will have to be made which take into account the needs and rights of both parents and child.

Management is called for in two areas of personal living – the physical or more practical side, and the psychological dimension.

4. Practical management

a) Health services

All disablements require access to adequate health services. The range of services needed will depend on the nature of the illness as well as on the person's individual circumstances. Some may also require the benefit of the social services. The emphasis in this section is deliberately on the self-help aspect of management. However, included in managing ourselves is knowing when and how to go about receiving outside help when it is appropriate to do so. The core of all health services is the GP. Being able to relate openly and with confidence to your own doctor is of paramount importance. Appreciating the knowledge and expertise of an expert, as well as valuing your own, establishes a healthy partnership relationship which is for your own good. Self-knowledge and professional knowledge should be viewed as complementary and never as competing. The numerous other services, be they hospital, in or outpatient, or community services, should be called on and utilised when necessary. Key personnel in the community services are the Public Health Nurses and the Home Helps. In addition there are the more specialized and limited groups of professionals such as physiotherapists, occupational therapists, social workers and others. Not to be forgotten is the very real help of relatives and neighbours. Such help can be both practical and supportive. It is very difficult to carry or manage a disability entirely on a 'go-it-alone' basis.

The more personally any of the above services are delivered, the more beneficial they are likely to be. Apart from the purely medical aspect of care, the other qualities needed by service providers are adequate time, good communication and rapport. When developing management expertise in their patients, health workers also need to be motivators and teachers. Managing a condition requires first of all knowledge about that condition and also acquiring the necessary skills, and this can only be achieved through tuition and practice. Management programmes should ideally be initiated by the experts, but over time a person learns ways and means of perfecting their own management techniques. A creative approach, having the courage which allows for mistakes and yet being able to learn from them, is a desirable quality to possess when managing disablements.

b) Some examples of managing particular disabilities

Everyone's situation is unique, but the following examples could indicate what is meant by managing a particular disablement. If deafness occurs (depending on its type) there is need to learn how to use a hearing aid and/or to lip-read. Deaf people will also need to learn to adjust to the many more hidden aspects of their disability, like not having the assistance of noise when crossing busy streets, learning to be more sensitive to the body language of others when one can no longer rely on words to pick up the subtleties in human relating, coping with the adverse reactions of other people, who may not always be as sensitive and tolerant as one would like to the problems and frustrations involved in hearing loss. Incontinence problems necessitate management such as the amount and timing of fluid intake and the use of incontinent wear if this is deemed necessary. Mis-managing this problem could include a person not taking enough fluids, or stopping socialising and leaving the house. Mobility problems necessitate learning to change the way tasks are performed. This could entail looking at items such as furniture, clothing, even the lay-out of the house, and changing to what is more suitable. It might involve the use of mechanical aids or gadgets. There are the simple aids like a walking stick and the more complex, such as a chair-lift. Simple adaptations to the house, such as rails, raised toilet seat, gadgets to assist dressing, bathing and eating, can make the difference between dependent and independent living. The assistance of an aid is commonly acceptable in the form of glasses or dentures, but many have difficulty when it comes to using others, like a stick or a wheelchair. Some have great difficulty in accepting the latter, shown in the not uncommon remark 'I would never allow myself to be seen in that'. Why this is so usually goes back to the level of acceptance and type of attitude adopted towards the illness. Such an attitude is also connected with people who are overly influenced by what other people say and think, or even by what they feel others might be thinking. Such surmisings may not be true, but are left unchecked and hence they remain unnecessary and unhelpful inhibiting factors in the management of problems. If our outlook is positive and our goal is to live as independently and as fully as is possible, then using aids of all kinds will be welcomed and not shunned as embarrassing.

c) Altering life-style

Altering life-style is always difficult, especially for those who are attached to longstanding routines and methods of doing things. The adjustment required might be very minor or it could be something that has major implications. Examples would be when it is no longer possible to drive the car, use the stairs so that the bed has to be moved downstairs, when one is no longer able to see the TV, or where there is the necessity to move to sheltered housing or a nursing home. If there is a need for residential care, it is desirable to explore what attractive options are available, for example, places where there are facilities for autonomy, privacy, intimacy, where some aspects of personal care can continue to be given by a close relative or friends if this is so desired, and where a creative, pleasing and homely atmosphere prevails. Knowing the general ethos and philosophy of care in a particular nursing home is necessary before a final choice is made.

Two key rehabilitation principles must be borne in mind on the question of assistance. The first is not to receive help before it is necessary, for example, if we can still carry out a task independently or are able to live independently in our own home. It may take longer to carry out tasks, and the assistance of a mechanical aid may be required, but the important thing, namely independence, is safeguarded. If help is needed, and this may be minimal or total, then receive it graciously, showing concern for the person who supplies it. Surveys reveal that of the 20% of older people who have some dependency problems, only 5% have high dependency needs; 10% have medium dependency needs, and 5% have low dependency needs, such as depending on someone to help with shopping.

d) Concern for the carer

If there is need for a carer, be they family or from an outside agency, it is vital to be attentive to the carer's well-being as well as your own. Over-demanding behaviour can be very destructive of this vital relationship for the cared-for person. It is necessary to achieve a healthy balance between both sides of the caring relationship. The carer needs to avoid undue pressure, even bullying tactics, and the person receiving the care requires sensitivity in avoiding over-demanding behaviour which could evoke an abusive reaction. In other words, a spirit of reasonableness must prevail where freedom and personal responsibility are valued both for yourself and for the other person in this special caring relationship. For example, if the family carer needs a break, it is not unreasonable that the person cared for avail of some form of respite facility. While this idea may not be relished, acceptance of such care for a short period is reasonable. More difficult is the decision to move to palliative care, long-term care or nursing home care situations, should dependency needs become too difficult to manage at home. Realism, courage and openness are called for as to what is the most appropriate form of care as a particular disability progresses, in relation to the resources that are available in the home and in the community. Placing unduly heavy demands on the personal lives of others is unreasonable. Many factors need to be considered when making a decision as to what is the most desirable form of care in a particular set of circumstances. Moving to a nursing home does not have to be seen as a last resort, a sentence, the end of our world. Some people positively opt for such a move, maintain a spirit of maximum independence in such a situation, and even discover opportunities for fuller living that were no longer possible while living at home. A spell in a nursing home may be a necessary stage in the transition from hospital to home.

e) Personal involvement and responsibility in decision-making

Decisions regarding the different types of care, and even the pros and cons of particular treatments, are more and more discussed between health professionals and their patients. Responsibility in having a say, and co-operating in difficult and often complex matters regarding our care, is something to be thought about in advance and is not a matter to be evaded as particular situations arise. Involvement in our own care, maintaining personal choice (even if the range of options is more restrictive than one would like) is desirable. Effective management is not about handing over total control to others. However, making decisions in this matter is often painful and requires adequate knowledge about the issues involved, as well as a degree of reasonableness towards yourself and the other people that will be affected by the decision.

f) Care of general health

Managing a disablement must also include care of our health in general. The preventative dimensions of care on issues in relation to fitness, adequate rest, appropriate weight level, as outlined in chapter two, need to be borne in mind. Part of general self-care is awareness – noticing changes that occur and attending to them in an appropriate way early on. 'A stitch in time saves nine.' An example of one area to notice and care for is our feet. Changes in skin colour, or temperature, as well as toe nails and breaks in the skin, can be significant. Often these are signs that show the early onset of circulation problems or diabetes. Foot-care requires suitable footwear, good hygiene and possibly the services of a chiropodist. Another example is care of our teeth. Poor eating habits can lead to undernutrition and this could be the result of some form of dental disability.

g) Maintenance of aids

A further aspect of management is the maintenance of aids. Examples would include seeing to the general upkeep and suitability of hearing aids, especially batteries; that glasses and dentures remain suitable, ferrules on a stick are in good condition; truss, collar, back and other support wear are replaced when worn; motorised wheel chairs and other more specialised equipment are serviced at regular intervals.

h) Safety

Safety issues are all part of good management. Included in this is the management of risk. It is undesirable to take unreasonable risks, but we can become over-cautious. If life is seen as an adventure then risk is always involved. Some people get nervous about themselves after an illness, so being firm yet kind with ourselves, and taking small positive steps to rebuilding confidence, is the way forward. If there have been falls, these can be so inhibiting that a person almost stops walking. The encouragement of others, planning manoeuvres with care and a prudent spirit of daring is, over time, what works best. Safety management also includes the elimination of risk hazards in the house and not carrying out tasks that are unsuitable to one's condition.

i) Managing pain

Learning to cope with pain is also a management issue. If pain is acute, medical attention and care is required. Chronic pain and discomfort largely call for self-management. The type and nature of the pain has a recognised pattern known to the person, as also is its cause – a particular diagnosis. Having a positive attitude regarding our ability to manage this pain, rather than letting the pain take control, is fundamental. Preventing chronic pain that interferes with living demands common sense, self-talk to get it in perspective, as well as at times putting distracting activities in place. Pain that is consciously focused on and is overly analysed often gets worse. Relief of chronic pain by the use of medication may be needed, but good self-help techniques may work as well, if not better. Some of these are often simple, such as altering position when sitting, lying or doing tasks that appear to aggravate pain, not staying in any one posture for too long, doing tasks differently or in stages, taking rest periods, altering diet – eating more or less of certain foods, practising some form of relaxation, indulging in something we enjoy, moving away from activities, at least temporarily, that are aggravating the pain.

5. Psychological management

Managing the practical issues connected with an illness is often the easiest part. Managing ourselves, our feelings and thoughts, as well as our significant relationships, is more complex. If there is an intimate relationship, the whole area of altered sexual behaviour that might become necessary has to be worked through with sensitivity by both partners in the relationship.

A fundamental matter in this regard is how we view our condition. Most illnesses are chronic and so a person is not really sick most of the time. The type of behaviour that results depends on perception. Some operate from wellness behaviour, others from sickness-type behaviour, and it is this basic difference that colours how we relate to ourselves and to others. Maintaining personal autonomy, freedom and the right to privacy are values to be insisted on, especially if those close to us tend to be over-protective. Being sensitive to others is also important and includes avoiding excusing ourselves because of our condition. During moments of frustration, which will be inevitable at times, we need to be wary that this is not unfairly directed against those who are close. Remaining alert to the needs of others, as well as to our own, is a balance that requires working at.

Older people who live alone can often be more resourceful, simply because there is no one else around to do things for them. On the reverse side, however, such people can become recluses in a way that is not normal or helpful for them. Bad habits can develop which let efforts at personal self-care, as well as normal social functioning, slip.

Managing the emotional and relationship issues connected with living with a disablement are the most difficult to deal with and hence they are receiving fuller consideration in the following chapter on managing stress.

CHAPTER FIVE

Managing the Stresses of Older Years

Stress is part and parcel of life, including the older years. It is our ability to cope with it that makes the difference between fulfilled and unfulfilled living. Learning to cope with the inevitable stresses of life involves understanding more clearly what stress is, what its effects are, and what are effective methods of coping with it.

What is stress?

The word stress has an engineering background. Materials are put under different stresses to discover their strength and durability. If the pressure or strain exerted is too great, there is a point at which the material will bend, crack or break. The same idea is used when talking about personal inner strength. If the pressures or strains of life become too great to cope with we can, in phrases commonly used, 'crack up' or 'break down'. It is difficult to define personal stress, but a possible definition is 'when we are pushed beyond comfortable limits'. Stress cuts across our sense of well-being to the extent that we no longer feel comfortable with ourselves. There is a good form of stress which is normally termed challenge. Artists, sports people, those working in projects they are interested in, often benefit by being stretched in order to give of their best. The stress written about here is bad stress or distress.

Often we are not sufficiently aware of our *level of stress* until it is quite severe, and then trying to manage it becomes increasingly difficult. When we are aware of our personal stress, we can pick up the warning signs early on. If we admit to it and do something early to remedy the situation, then much suffering can be prevented.

The *consequences of stress* are many and varied, the predominant one being that a lot of joy goes out of living, with positive feelings receding and negative ones taking over. A severe result of uncoped-with stress is break-down or burn-out. Those who find their final years at work particularly stressful might enter their retirement period in a state of burn-out, which might call for a period of rest and possibly professional help before fuller living can emerge and the positive aspects to ageing begin to be both appreciated and lived.

Our *stress threshold* varies over life, even over one day. To an extent it depends on the multiplicity of stresses that can come together at any one time. We may be coping well with a major crisis and then something small happens, the threshold is crossed, and we can no longer manage. In other words, we have gone beyond the tolerable limit. Stress is present from the teenage years on, and each period of life, while containing the stresses common to all periods, has also its own particular stresses to contend with. If the art of coping with stress has been developed over life, then we are fortunate in having this skill to rely on when coping with the particular stresses of the older years.

Understanding the three *sources of stress* can be helpful:

The first source is the environment, that is, anything outside of ourselves, including places, things, people, circumstances, events. The physical surroundings in which we live can be pleasing or act as a stressor. An untidy kitchen, diminished personal living space, a dark room, a dirty house, drab buildings, lack of colour, no plants in a house or trees in a neighbourhood, can all be potential stressors. However, relating to other people remains the most common source of stress. Personal circumstances and events can also act as profound stressors.

A second source of stress, as already noted, is our own body. If we are not comfortable with our body as it ages, then we live with a constant source of irritation. If there is some disease or disability in addition, and this is not accepted, then our body becomes an even greater source of stress.

The third source of stress, and the commonest cause of it, is our own thoughts. Personal thoughts label how we perceive and interpret life's happenings. Places, events and relationships have no emotional content. It is our thinking which evokes the type of feelings that are aroused. Stress is often the result of 'twisted thinking patterns', such as prejudices, tunnel vision, black and white depiction, exaggeration.

Our thoughts flow from our beliefs, values and attitudes. Beliefs change slowly and imperceptibly; core beliefs tend to last a lifetime. Regarding values, people notice that over the years their values change, sometimes radically, sometimes in small ways, and some values remain constant. Looking back over a decade or more, we discover possibly that values we previously held as sacrosanct are no longer so. Changes are noticed only over a period of time; the change as it occurs is largely imperceptible. Attitudes, on the other hand, can be changed more easily as we consciously set to work, challenging ourselves on some of our personal attitudes. This involves checking out with ourselves why we have adopted certain attitudes to see if they are true, fair to the person or situation as it really is. By deliberately standing back and objectively looking at ourselves in relation to a person, circumstances, or events, we can decide to alter particular attitudes. The change is not easy. It happens for us in the very act of understanding, as we stand back and see things in new and different ways.

Stresses arise from four different types of situations:

In the first place are sudden unexpected events like an accident, an illness, a death of someone close. It is appropriate at such times to be under stress, but it is also normal to work through the stress in a reasonable period of time.

A second category are those associated with entering a new stage in life such as retirement, leaving one's home to go and live with a relative or in a retirement home or a nursing home. Learning to live with a disability is in this second category, as well as learning to cope with the disability of a spouse or other close family relative with whom one lives. It takes time to adjust to the new situation and requires us to be gentle with ourselves as we move into an altered lifestyle.

Thirdly, there are the stresses of everyday life, like difficulties in relationships, worrying about one's children or grandchildren, financial concerns.

Finally, the unconscious self can be a source of stress. Hidden anxieties, fears, hurts, resentments, can emerge at any stage throughout life and especially in our older years when the unfinished business of earlier times calls for attention. Such buried feelings can be resurrected unexpectedly by almost anything, such as the death of a sibling, even by looking at old photographs. Some of these feelings may have been buried since childhood, when they were too difficult to face. Help may be necessary to cope with these and other feelings connected with the darker side of ourselves.

There is a close connection between our mental and physical health. For example, if we have the 'flu, or have broken a limb, we will feel down in ourselves at least at times during the period of recovery. The period of convalescence may prove more stressful than the acute period. Conversely, if we are psychologically low, as after a bereavement, we are more prone to physical ailments. It is now generally accepted that the psycho-somatic dimension plays a large part in illness. Recovery from sickness or learning to live with a disablement takes longer and is less complete if there are stresses not adequately coped with.

The first stage in coping with stress is to be aware we are under stress and take responsibility for this fact. Following on from that, it is helpful to be able to identify the source(s) as specifically as possible. For instance, to say one's stress comes from a relationship, one's physical environment, or a particular disablement is too general. There is need to find out what precisely are the factors in the situation that make it bothersome and to name these.

The effects of stress

The effects of stress are numerous and they vary from person to person. Being aware of the early onset of stress, by knowing our personal signs and symptoms, can help minimise its effect, provided such signs are taken seriously and we do something to alleviate the situation. The more common signs and symptoms can be categorised under the physical, emotional, intellectual and spiritual aspects of our lives (categories already familiar when speaking of wellbeing). Several symptoms are likely to be present if the stress level is severe.

Physical symptoms include the following: tiredness which is not related to levels of activity; sleeplessness, either going to sleep with difficulty or wakening early; headaches (sometimes referred to as tension headaches); stomach pains; chest tightness; vague aches and pains, especially in the neck and shoulders, palpitations, breathlessness and sweating. Such symptoms could mean there is an underlying physical disorder which would require checking with a doctor. If, however, nothing is discovered and you are in a known stressful situation and this symptom has been noticed before in other stressful periods, then stress is likely to be the cause of these symptoms and the treatment required is to manage the stress.

Emotional symptoms which are commonly experienced when under stress are: feeling edgy, irritable, drained; negative feelings predominating; inability to manage your feelings as you normally would, such as crying becoming intense sobbing; failing to overcome emotional upsets in a normal time span, for example, where anxiety, anger, sadness linger or where our reaction is out of proportion to the cause, such as losing your temper over some small incident.

Intellectual signs can be significant and they include: inability to concentrate, listlessness, racing thoughts, pre-occupation with the traumatic event, lack of interest in things, a general sense of apathy, nightmares.

Spiritual symptoms can also act as indicators of stress. These could be a persistent inner restlessness; searching for meaning in events and in your own life; unconnected outer and inner self; life not in tune with your inner desires; wrestling with suffering and pain, physical or emotional; scruples.

Changes in normal patterns of behaviour could indicate the presence of stress. For instance, addictive behaviours usually increase – a person drinks or smokes more than is normal. Eating habits can alter – some eat more, others less. Some people become tight with money, others over-spend. It is not uncommon to find older people who are over-concerned about money and constantly count money or check their financial affairs. This could be stress-related or an early sign of dementia. A lack of attention to personal appearance might indicate the presence of stress. If stress is severe, a person can become withdrawn.

Knowing the *signs of stress in a relationship* can be helpful. Such signs could be showing an absence of gestures of affection; entering a pursuing/distancing cycle in the relationship; resorting to manipulation tactics; small problems becoming catastrophes; having difficulty in acknowledging needs without blaming the other person.

Why some physical symptoms appear as a result of stress is due to the way our bodies work. There are two systems involved in a stress situation: the nervous system (the unconscious part) and the endocrine or gland system. In acute stress, an alarm reaction is aroused in the body and this is sometimes termed the fight/flight response. The body does not distinguish between stress and fear, so when we are under stress the body reacts as if it had a fright and hence the fight/flight reaction is aroused. Because of circumstances and conditioning we tend to do neither. However, the alarm warning has gone off and this results in a higher level of adrenalin in the body which has certain effects. It causes the heart to beat faster and blood pressure to rise. Breathing quickens and muscles tighten, ready to spring to action. Without such action the muscle tightness tends to settle in three areas: the shoulders are raised, and the teeth and hands clench. The skin can sweat and emptying the bladder becomes an urgent need.

Symptoms of heart thumping, sweating, breathlessness are seen in panic attacks as well as in fears and phobias. Fears and phobias can be acute realities in the lives of some older people – for example some are terrified of being burgled, or, if they do go out, they are fearful of being attacked. Others are fearful that their home will be taken from them. In more chronic stress situations, such symptoms may not be visible, but there is a low level of arousal, with an increase in adrenalin which, if persistent, can cause harm.

Managing stress well plays a large part in the level of wellbeing we experience. It is not the frequency or intensity of stress that is the most significant; it is our ability to cope with it that makes the difference. This second stage in coping is important since it enables us to recognise and be alert to the signs and symptoms which show us that stress is there. It then requires us to take responsibility for doing something about it. Signs and symptoms differ – the important thing is to know our own.

Ways of managing stress

Being able to name our stresses, as well as knowing their signs and symptoms, leads to the third and final stage of developing ways of coping with it. This requires understanding, determination and practice. It means taking personal responsibility for our mental health. Coping, managing stress, is not just about surviving, but is concerned with living fully and positively. Each of us has to manage our own coping; it is not something that can be done by others, no matter how supportive they may be. Some people appear to cope better than others; everyone copes better at certain times; no one copes all the time.

Managing stress has to be learnt, and taking control of our lives and the various happenings that unfold is the key. An attitude of trying to manage our stresses, rather than letting them take control, is the first step. Stress worsens when people feel helpless and feel that they have no control over an issue, incident or relationship. This is never in fact true, as there is always something that can be done to reduce the stress effect. At times this will involve being pro-active, making things happen rather than always letting things happen. Learning from past experiences of success and failure can help us see what we can do for ourselves, as well as when it might be preferable to get outside help.

There are some people who hold onto their stresses and become martyrs, in a way similar to some who hold onto their mental or physical illnesses because they cannot face life 'well'. Being in the martyr place can unconsciously be a way of getting attention, but it is a sad and diminishing way to live.

Before examining specific coping strategies, it is essential to stand back and see if the source of the stress can be removed or lessened in some way. This may not be possible where a terminal illness is diagnosed, one is growing old, or a grandchild is born with a congenital disability. In such instances, perceptions and attitudes have to change and this takes time as altered meanings and a deepening of insight develop. Most situations, however, can be changed, even radically. Major changes may be involved like moving out of home; or much smaller things may have to change, such as changing timetables, home rituals, ways of doing things. People may often complain about things without considering what can be done to ease matters, even in some small way, or going to others who could do something to lessen the stress. There are often many ways of getting around a problem. For example when you discover you can no longer drive, that does not have to mean that you are housebound. Even if public transport is no longer usable either, taking the occasional taxi, or receiving or asking sometimes for a lift from neighbours, friends or voluntary organisations is usually a real possibility. Some creative thinking is called for. It is sad to see people constantly complaining and yet doing nothing about the problem.

Everyone has to discover for themselves effective ways of coping with stress that work for them, and put these into practice. Below are set out twelve psychological strategies, and nine more specific physical approaches that are helpful.

1. Psychological ways that help in managing stress

– The first and most important is *learning the ability to live reflectively*. This means allowing time and space to know what is happening in your inner world. It enables you to become sensitive to early signs of stress, and as to whether personal needs are being adequately met. Growth in self-knowledge is a great asset in life. In order to tune in daily to your internal radio and hear what it is saying, certain steps have to be taken. Ideally, everyone should set aside some personal time for themselves everyday and in a space that allows for privacy with no interruptions. Many people find this difficult, so starting with short ten-minute periods or less could prove beneficial.

– *Admitting that stress is there* is an obvious step towards coping with stress. As with alcoholics and others, nothing can be done until the problem is admitted and reality faced. Depending on an individual's previous history and experiences, there may be the expectation on the part of others that a particular person has been and is a good coper. Inevitably, some of the stresses of the older years are different and hence have not been previously encountered. Admitting to stress is not admitting to failure. In fact, it could show strength of character and a sense of realism.

– *Talking the matter over with someone*, whether relative, friend, or professional, is a well recognized way of helping. It requires more than just talking 'about' the issue. It is helpful if, during the conversation, you come to discover and name as specifically as possible exactly what the problem is, and also to name the feeling that is present as a result of the stress. For instance, if you were deeply hurt, then say that, and don't soften it by saying you were 'a bit put out'. If one is in the listener role, that is all about listening, and not giving advice. At a later stage it might be possible and helpful to indicate impartially other courses of action. Developing good support systems in life, such as friendships, is desirable for everyone so that there is someone to turn to in crisis moments. It is also helpful if you are aware of possible low points or moments, such as seasons of the year or anniversaries, and seek out appropriate supports around such times.

– *Trying to be objective* about what has actually happened to cause stress, whether it arises from an event or a relationship, is not easy. When you are calm, it is useful to try and stand back and view the problem as if you were standing in someone else's shoes. When as objective a stance as is possible is reached, then there is need to face what has happened and see what requires changing and what has to be accepted. There is a tendency, when under stress, either to blame others or to blame yourself. Staying in the blaming place does not help you to cope; trying to be objective in order to gain insight into the reality of what has happened does.

– *Being open to seeing things differently* follows from the above. You need to challenge yourself to see if your personal views and interpretations are correct. Questions like 'Am I being too rigid, too narrow in my thinking?' or 'Am I prejudiced?' can be helpful. Watching the use of certain words like 'must', 'should', 'ought' is indicative. Often people use these words of themselves or others, for example 'I must do this', or 'He should do that'. Such statements need to be challenged by further questions, 'Why must I do this?' or 'Why should he have to do that?' The only 'must' in life is not to harm ourselves or others; everything else is relative. It is desirable that we do many things in life, but they are not absolute imperatives.

– *Aiming not to give in to negative thinking* is vital. Negative thoughts are likely to come when you are under stress, but the important things is not to 'nurse' these, but instead to try and move as quickly as possible from the 'poor me', 'why me' place. Watching your inner conversation is useful. Often your self-talk is negative, especially if you are low. Phrases like 'I'm no good, no one really cares about me, I'm too old, no one is interested in my opinions anymore', can surface. If you feed on negative thoughts, this can lead to expecting unpleasant things to happen and so the stress level gets worse.

– *Trying to take a positive approach*, and beginning by taking one small step, loosens the grip of the negative. Beginning with a shift towards positive self-talk helps: 'I'm OK', 'I'm OK despite my inadequacies, uncertainties', 'I value my opinions and the wisdom I have gained over the years'. The problem on hand may be difficult and the way forward unclear, but it is important to start somewhere and to begin by taking one small step. Doing nothing is not an option in managing stress.

– *Setting goals and making action plans* is a practical way to cope with stress. There are always alternative ways of looking at and doing things, so examining options and setting priorities, and having the courage to try out new things, are steps that need to be taken. The decisions need to be specific and to have a time-scale built into them. For example, 'I will have my main meal in the middle of the day starting next Monday'; 'I will go and see the solicitor about my will this week'; 'Tomorrow I will phone to arrange to have the services of a home help twice a week'.

– *Searching out relevant information* to deepen understanding can considerably reduce stress. Not knowing, not having sufficient information about something, raises anxiety levels which can add to the existing stress. Often when the truth is known, even if it brings bad news, it can also bring a sense of relief, since there is no longer the feeling of being in the dark. Fear of the unknown, especially if something sinister is anticipated, is always stressful, so again information regarding knowing what to expect in particular circumstances can considerably reduce stress.

– *Looking for something positive* is always helpful. In acute stress this may be difficult, but where there is chronic stress this can be very beneficial. People speak of the new friends they have made in and through their difficulties, of the things they have learnt about themselves, of how their values have changed for the better, of how they have gained tolerance and been given an insight into suffering that they would otherwise never have known.

– *Learning the art of saying goodbye* is often necessary in the stresses of life. What is required may involve a letting go of people, places, pets, tasks. The process of letting go and moving on is painful. However, it is only by entering the pain and going through it that we discover this is the way out of the stress. As I said earlier, letting go, saying goodbye, involves loss, and it is important to grieve adequately over these losses in order that you can move on.

– *Setting realistic goals* plays a large part in both preventing and coping with the stresses ingrained in the ordinary everyday happenings of life.

First of all, there are the goals we set for ourselves. We can set goals that are unrealistically high, as may happen a perfectionist. When personal expectations are too high, and they are not achieved, negative feelings are aroused. People become despondent, worry and then feel guilty because they do not achieve or do as much as they think they ought. What is demanded of each of us is to do what is reasonably possible, no more or no less. And even if we do fall short of what is reasonable, the managing of such a failure can become something positive. If a person is unable to deliver on over-high standards, managing is not about coping with failure, but it is about setting realistic standards for the future.

Secondly, we can allow others to make unrealistic demands on us, expecting us to be or act in certain ways. This can happen in all relationships and especially in close ones. It is important not to take these unrealistic expectations on board. We need to know our limits and not to allow ourselves to become over-stretched by another person. It is undesirable for anyone to be constantly subject to the unrealistic expectations of another person.

Finally, setting unrealistic goals for others can also cause stress. Parents, for example, can sometimes do this with their children. Apart from being unhelpful for the son or daughter, it is also unhelpful to the parent who will have to cope with feelings of disappointment, of being let down. Such feelings can last for years, causing persistent stress.

2. Physical ways that help in managing stress

– *Enjoyment* is a great stress reducer. In the present over-serious western world there is need to develop the 'playful' side of ourselves and to be aware that enjoyment is an essential component to living fully. It is never too late to learn this important dimension of life. It is particularly necessary not to allow ourselves become so low and despondent that we can no longer enjoy anything. Enjoyment is often not connected with the exotic, but rather the simple things of life, like a walk, talking to a friend, enjoying a flower.

– *Leisure activities* are something we enjoy doing, but they are done on a regular basis and so discipline is necessary to partake in such activities on the days we do not feel like participating. Adherence to a leisure activity can both prevent and considerably lessen the stresses of life.

– *Moving out of the environment* is sometimes indicated as part of stress management. In an emergency situation, for instance after a serious quarrel, it can be useful to escape for a while in order to cool off and stand back from what has happened. A days' outing, a weekend away, holidays, are all beneficial in times of stress. Everything tends to be seen differently after a break away from our normal environment.

– *Doing one thing at a time* without rushing enables us to get into the present moment. Being at what we are at a particular moment in time can be very therapeutic. This is especially necessary during times of acute stress when it is difficult to settle down to anything.

– *Putting energy into things we like doing and do well* is valuable with acute forms of stress. Such moments are not the time to tackle difficult and unpleasant tasks. It is also not the time to put ourselves in circumstances where over-reaction is possible. For example, if a person has recently been bereaved or separated, social events in the early days following such events need to be chosen with thought.

– *Knowing and holding onto 'anchor points'* helps in both acute and chronic stress. These could be places (a favourite spot), relationships (especially those that restore confidence and bring life), activities that we enjoy (for example, gardening, going to a film, a daily routine).

– *Doing something for someone else* can be a good stress reducer. This might seem strange for someone who is very incapacitated by a severe illness or disability, yet it truth is for everyone. The doing may be a task, like visiting someone, or making a phone call, or even a reaching out in concerned thought to the needs of others. Such activity helps to restore a sense of perspective to our own problems when we bring into our awareness the problems of another person or persons.

– *Looking after our general health* is required by everyone but this is particularly necessary during periods of stress. Adequate rest, exercise, and diet must be attended to with more care. If our physical health is in reasonable order this will enhance a sense of well-being which in turn enables us to cope better with stress.

– *Relaxation exercises* are often the first thing that comes to people's minds when stress is spoken about. While coping with stress demands much more than being able to relax, relaxation exercises are helpful to many people.

There are a large number of techniques available but all include certain basics, which are as follows:

1. Take up a comfortable, well-supported posture, ideally lying down or well supported in an arm chair.

2. Set a quiet atmosphere, without too much light, and with sufficient heat.

3. Give sufficient time, twenty minutes minimum, to arrive at a reasonable level of relaxation. There is no such thing as instant relaxation.

4. Close your eyes and listen to your breathing. Do not change the rhythm, just listen to it and go with it. This can be done for most, or all, of the exercise.

5. Other techniques can be added but are not essential.

CHAPTER SIX

The Satisfaction of the Older Years

'There is only one art and that is the art of living.' These are striking words, coming particularly from someone who was himself
an artist, a poet – W. B. Yeats. Living is indeed an art, an art-form
which is perfected and receives its final touches in our older
years. The tapestry of our life may take on unexpected designs
and blending of colours if the latter decades are lived in a spirit
of adventure, creativity and heightened awareness. While, for
some, these years may have moments of exuberance and ecstasy,
for many it is more likely to be a time of quieter discoveries
where 'there lives the dearest freshness deep down things'
spoken of by Gerard Manley Hopkins. It is a time of opportunity
for re-awakening the fresh child-like wonder of discovering
truth and beauty in ways that up to now were only glimpsed at.

Chapter Two discussed the question of answering human needs
in a reasonable and integrated manner. These needs can be further divided into those elementary ones which are necessary for
living, and those needs which enable me to flourish as a human
person, as the unique individual that I am. Our older years
allow us to taste this experience of flourishing in new and richer
ways than in previous years where often such experiences were
transient. This sense of fulfilment will not be as present to those
who suffer from depression, but this is not to deny that the possibility is open to everyone, especially if we expect it and do
what we can to facilitate it happening.

When younger, or in the middle years, most people get caught
up in earning a living, developing a career, raising a family.
With such responsibilities now in the main over, there is the possibility of concentrating more fully on the art of living in a more

conscious way. It is not a question of doing a whole lot of things for this to happen (although it could include that), but rather it is a case of experiencing more deeply whatever we do. So much of life is inevitably lived at a superficial level, but now the challenge is to greater quality in our being and doing, as opposed to sheer quantity. Inherent in this new perspective is a movement from a life of complexity towards one of a rich simplicity. The best experiences, as we continue on our maturing journey, are likely to be the simple ones like a good conversation with a friend, examining a leaf, listening to the sound of children at play, taking the dog for a walk, luxuriating in a bath, reading afresh a favourite poem.

The experience of satisfaction in our older years contains within it the knowledge that our present experience of living is in the main what we want it to be. It might not be what we earlier envisaged it might be, yet the reality of life as it is now can truly be described as personally satisfying. Satisfaction, like other qualities connected with human living, is a relative concept, is experienced in varying degrees of intensity, and is always open to constant fluctuations. Satisfaction in life implies a sense of contentedness, which, while never complete, is an experience that can be named as our normal state of being. Anxieties, fears, and all the range of other negative emotions will come and go, but the pre-dominant one that remains is that of satisfaction or contentment.

There is a growing awareness, particularly among health care professionals and researchers, of the importance of quality of life (QoL) as an important evaluation of health status both pre- and post-medical interventions. There is no agreement as to how quality of life can be measured precisely because it is based on an individual's personal assessment of life experience. Since it is by its very nature a self-report, it defies external set measurements. The Royal College of Surgeons in Dublin, in conjunction with St James Hospital, did a survey on healthy groups of younger and older people. While the concerns of younger and older groups obviously differed, it was discovered to the surprise of some that older respondents were in general happier with their lives than the younger group. Younger people may pity older people, not realising that many who are old are getting more out of life than they are themselves.

The QoL evaluation is also being used in assessing the outcome of elective surgical procedures like joint replacement and coronary artery by-pass grafts. It is not solely technical success that is measured, but also the subsequent quality of life experienced by the person. Life satisfaction scales can be reasonably high, even in older people who have health problems. A survey done in Wales of a group of seventy-five to ninety-nine-year-olds, showed that nine people out of ten felt their health was good, at least 'alright' for their age, even though three quarters of this group were limited by their physical condition.

The experience of satisfaction, like happiness, cannot be attained per se. It is the by-product or result of our attitudes, values, lifestyle. Satisfaction can, however, be facilitated by certain measures and three in particular will be mentioned here. Other ways have been discussed in chapter three on retirement. The areas treated here are: Remaining a contributor to society in some way, no matter how small; living a life of greater awareness through a heightened use of our senses; and a greater exposure to the world of the arts.

Remaining a contributor to society

Remaining a giver has been previously touched on, but it cannot be over emphasised. A key satisfaction in living for all age groups lies in concern for others and especially those in need. The joy in giving, in being able to love people and our world, remains the core of fulfilled living. If we deny ourselves this side of living, life itself will become empty, because one of the prime ingredients to experiencing life as fulfilling is missing. In addition to often needing the support of others as we age, there is also the need in turn to be a supporter, at least emotionally, of those who are close to us. The actual ways we reach out to others are unique to each one, but the need both to give and receive love is fundamental to every human person.

Living a life of awareness through a heightened use of our senses

All of us live limited lives. We never develop our potential any-
where near what is possible, largely due to our lack of awareness. Fulfilled living is about living with greater awareness and
this is closely linked with both our outer and inner senses. Our
outer and inner senses are also intimately connected with each
other – seeing with insight; hearing with inner listening; touching with sensitivity; tasting with inner relish; smelling with
inner savouring of intangible realities.

A strange paradox is noticeable in our older years, namely, that
as our senses diminish in physiological acuteness, our appreciation and wonderment at such gifts and endowments often grow.
The senses are the pinnacle of all our bodily functions, powers,
and abilities. They are the way through which we learn all we
know. They are also the way through which we communicate
with each other and the world. If we are totally deprived of one
or more of these senses, we are truly deprived of enormous
sources of enrichment. The senses are par excellence the gate-
way to full living, and the older years provide the time and opportunity to enter this gate and enjoy the marvels that are to be
found in every human situation. Earlier in life we may have
been too functional and so missed many things, simply because
we did not discover the enrichment of really looking, seeing,
hearing, smelling and touching. Moving from mind to sense
helps restore this often largely lost dimension to living. For
those who want it, the older years can be a time for developing
our perceptual self, our powers of perceiving reality, what is really real around us. Doing this can lead us to an experience similar to that of Howard Carter when he peered into the tomb of
Tutankamun for the first time in 4,000 years: 'I see marvellous
things.' Sense living helps us to de-familiarise the familiar,
which is always rich for those whose sense life is open to the
macro and micro world both around us and within. Patrick
Kavanagh says it succinctly as only a true poet can: 'Ordinary
things have lovely wings.'

Developing further our sense-life calls for certain behaviours
and attitudes. The *first* of these is time and the ability to stop

rushing. More positively, it means making time 'to stand and stare' so that we can really hear, touch, taste, smell. *Secondly*, it calls for an outlook which is awake, one that is ready for surprises and the unexpected, and a preparedness to drop plans in order to capture and savour the unexpected moment – the happening that presents itself for full attention. *Thirdly*, it requires watching our fatigue levels, since tiredness dulls awareness and thus it means taking adequate periods of rest. *Fourthly*, it means appreciating and caring adequately for our sense organs – eyes, ears, taste buds, skin, nose – and related aids – spectacles, hearing aids, dentures. *Finally*, our senses are aroused by stimulation and those senses whose function is becoming diminished may need the assistance of increased stimulation. For example, our sense of smell can weaken, so deliberately setting out to smell, particularly pleasant and pungent scents, can be helpful in keeping this sense alive and even reawakening it to what previously went unnoticed. The same can be done for taste by adding different or slightly stronger flavours to food.

Our outer senses, as already said, link with a set of inner senses. Coming to our senses can arouse in us a sense of wonder, awe, and delight at what is without as well as what lies within. When we *see* colour, shape, size, form – for example, a sunset, the hand of a newborn child, a work of art – we expand our insight to truth and beauty. When we really *hear* sounds – bird song, music, the human voice – in all their rich variety of tone, volume and texture, we enlarge our powers of inner listening to the spoken and unspoken, to the inner and outer voices, to the riches of silence as well as sound. When we *taste* our food or drink, and its texture and flavours, we learn inner relishing, that capacity to delight in things, people, places, events, truth, beauty. When we *smell*, both the pleasant and unpleasant, we arouse in ourselves an inner awareness of the ephemeral or intangible such as becoming sensitive to atmosphere in a situation, or experience the power of association that links us to the past, as well as to the exotic. When we *touch*, we discover hardness, softness, shape, texture, hot or cold, and are awakened to similar inner qualities in ourselves and others. Touch, possibly the most sacred organ of all because of its power to communicate intimacy, is the sense organ that is left intact in most people until their death. We freely touch the small baby, and instinctively most people feel free to touch the dying person. Sadly, some people are inhibited in their use and receiving of touch, and hence miss the richness inherent in this particular sense.

Touch, and all our senses, are given to be used fully, freely and appropriately. They help to protect by, for example, alerting us to danger, but pre-eminently they are there for communication, appreciation, enjoyment. The greatest adventure of our older years may be found in the unfathomable riches discovered in the simple opening of ourselves to the world of what our own senses have to offer us. There is a sense of wonderment too in being aware of ourselves in our act of appreciation. This was so strong for the psalmist that he exclaimed: 'For the wonder of my being I thank you.'

Exposure to the world of the arts

The satisfactions of the older years can be greatly enhanced by exposure to the arts – an exposure of depth rather than quantity. Many of us, especially in the West, have had experiences of varying kinds and often the sheer variety fosters a certain super-ficiality. How many books, films can we really recall? – probably only the few whose impact we were open to and which said something particularly significant to us. The older years are a time to select and savour what really attracts us in the line of music, poetry, drama, painting, literature, dance and other art forms. 'We have forgotten who and what we are and art makes us remember what we have forgotten.' (G.K. Chesterton) Being free to expose oneself to the new, or returning to the old and known, is what matters so that the experience is one that is per-sonally enriching and delight-filled. Such activity lends itself to stretching our imagination which may have been suppressed in earlier times by the humdrum of life. A fresh releasing of our imaginative powers can prove very freeing. It can also reveal a creative side to ourselves, even to becoming an inventor.

The art experience has two forms of expression – we can devel-op our appreciation of art, or enter the creation of art ourselves.

For example, we can read, or try writing; view paintings, or paint; listen to music or compose. Re-entering or trying dance or free movement for the first time, even in our eighties, can be truly liberating and can help to integrate a growth in inner freedom with body freedom. The act of creating, whether dancing, laying out a garden, sculpting or whatever, can be one of life's most satisfying experiences. It is fortunately not uncommon for older people to discover for the first time talents they never knew existed, or to build on talents which up to now have largely lain dormant. A quotation from Pablo Casals, the great Spanish musician, re-enforces all that has been said:

> 'On my last birthday I was ninety-three. This is not young, of course ... but age is a relative matter. If you continue to work and absorb the beauty of the world about you, you find that age does not necessarily mean getting old. I feel many things more intensely than before and for me life grows more fascinating .... The man who works is never bored, is never old. Work and interest in worthwhile things are the best remedy for age. Each day I am re-born. Each day I must begin again.'

This remarkable approach to life of someone at ninety-three echoes well the words of the Old Testament prophet Isaiah written in the 7th century B.C.: 'Now I am revealing new things to you, things hidden and unknown to you, created just now, this very moment, of these things you have heard nothing until now, so that you cannot say, "O yes, I knew all this."'

In the last decades of life, many do develop fresh and absorbing interests, fall in love and in general discover excitement and newness in an endless number of ways. Browning has the lovely lines:

> 'Grow old along with me; for the best is yet to be'.

CHAPTER SEVEN

Ageing in Wisdom, Hope and Joy

This chapter attempts to bring together many of the strands related to ageing already referred to in this book while focusing in a special way on the experience of wisdom, hope and joy in our older years. We have only one life cycle to live and, as we grow older, the realization comes that it is the actual living of life that is the source of our wisdom, hope and joy. As we move on towards fulfilling the cycle of our lives, what is experienced as true and authentic assumes greater relevance and importance. No book on ageing would be complete if it did not endeavour to explore wisdom, hope, joy, which can and often do emerge as important values in the latter part of life.

Ageing is a process of growth which, as it unfolds, can slowly reveal to us the great mystery that life is for all of us. The journey of living is normally towards simplicity and hopefully to a greater capacity to give, until ultimately the call for all is the giving up of our own lives in the form we know it. Older people who live fully are great prophets, who can enable those less mature to enter more deeply into the mystery of living. Fulfilled ageing allows us to discover more and more life's treasures and, par excellence, the wonder of what it is to be a unique and fully alive human being. Ageing is therefore a time for hope, not despair; a time for maturing in wisdom, not for personal diminishment; a time for enjoyment, not for colourless living.

Wisdom

The Wisdom literature of the Old Testament, written over two thousand years ago, is full of gems about the nature and qualities of wisdom, such as: 'Wisdom is bright and does not grow dim. By those who love her she is readily seen and found by those who look for her.' The wisdom spoken of is very much wisdom of the heart so that wisdom and love are closely related; indeed, mature love's flower is wisdom. One often hears 'He/she has matured with the years.' It is this mellowing of the person, especially shown in their ability to love well, with integrity, that makes a person wise. Mature love is likened to rich red wine; it is a love which grows in depth and perspective, being refined in the furnace of the cycle of one's own life lived fully.

Another well-known Wisdom passage says:

There is a season for everything:
> A time for giving birth, a time for dying;
> a time for planting, a time for uprooting what has been planted;
> a time for knocking down, a time for building;
> a time for tears, a time for laughter;
> a time for mourning, a time for dancing; ...
> a time for keeping, a time for throwing away;
> a time for keeping silent, a time for speaking,
> a time for loving, ... a time for peace.

The older years are a time for all these things, and it is above all the wisdom of love that discerns the truth of what each moment offers as it unfolds. Wisdom is considered one of the special fruits of the older years which allows us to live with a certain harmony and contentedness amidst the many complexities of life. It has been said: 'There is need for the rehabilitation of wisdom. It is not fashionable today, especially its vital, dynamic, creative nature. The Chinese know more of wisdom than other races and compare it to wind and lightning – it rushes headlong and irresistibly on its way and cannot be stopped or laid hold of; it purifies the air like lightning and strikes when there is need of it. Wisdom has the power to play with opposites, establishing a synthesis as opposed to compromise.'

The latter decades of life are a time to let go of many things, and one is the world of compromise to finding more and more a synthesis and integration in our lives. The ability to live in greater simplicity and serenity, in the midst of paradox and complexity, is the fruit of wisdom. Wisdom can be found in the young as well as the old, but it is more likely to emerge as a person matures with age. Wisdom flows from growth in our personal experience of what it is to be truly human, and the older years are a special time to complete the task of discovering what being human is truly about.

One way of dividing the human journey is to view it in four stages. The first decade is all about the child exploring what it is to be human. The second stage, which can cover many decades, is about discovering our individuality and this includes within it the desire to achieve, to be significant in some way, shown by the various positions we adopt within society. The third stage, which often emerges in the later middle or earlier older years, can carry the note of a more serious spiritual quest, where there is a movement from achievement to that of finding meaning. The fourth and final stage is about an enriched experience of the first stage, namely it is about living more fully our own humanity.

The fourth stage partly emerges from a growing awareness of one's own vulnerability. As Jung would say, it is about being more in touch with our 'shadow', the darker side of ourselves, while at the same time being in tune with our inner strengths. Discovering the opposites in ourself, and developing 'the power to play with' these, helps to form an integrated self and this is part of the growth process of the older years. It is linked with the search for meaning and fulfilment which is an essential component of a person who remains a searcher for truth. Einstein says: 'The man who regards his life as meaningless, is not merely unhappy but hardly fit to live.' The search for what life is about affects us all through life, becoming more pressing at times and particularly in moments of crisis. This search can be very acute for young people but also for some older people. An inability to discover meaning is more likely to occur in those who are depressed or people who suffer from severe frailty. Seeing the point to life can, for some, become a very real issue and may tempt a person to try or actually to commit suicide. (Alas, suicide in the older population is a growing phenomenon.)

Wisdom includes being in touch not only with our own evolving sense of what it is to be human, but also involves the ability to stay in touch with the humanity of others – both those close to us and humankind in general. This is what compassion is all about. This means being able to rejoice with all the human experiences we know to be good, while allowing ourselves to be disturbed by the inhumanity we touch both in ourselves and others. Growth in awareness also includes being in touch with the created world and doing our bit to foster nature's ecological balance.

Wisdom comes to people in innumerable ways. We associate this gift with artists, mystics, philosophers, gurus, while at the same time it has always been recognised that it can be found among simple and formally uneducated people. Largely, wisdom emerges from people who are reflective – reflective about what lies deep in themselves as well as living with a reflective awareness of all that is outside the self, namely other people, ideas, issues, creation, art in all its forms. At certain moments in the older years, people are likely to take stock of themselves and look back over life from whatever the present stage may be for them. Part of this process is to own our own history, which is largely influenced by the many choices we have made over life. Endo, the Japanese novelist says: 'Just as with all interpersonal relationships in our life we are made to suffer by those things we have chosen, it is in confronting our choices we gradually discover ourselves.' The discovery of self is always on-going and is very much part of growth in wisdom. We are never static, and maybe it is in our older old years that the most major changes, as well as the major discoveries, are made. The human spirit has unfathomable capacity for truth, beauty, freedom and love. The person who remains open to reality, to life, despite possible diminished functional ability and increasing fatigue, can be ready to imbibe, absorb, experience the new in ways that are both painful and enriching. Growth always involves some pain as well as enrichment. If the mind remains alert and a spirit of awareness and reflectiveness is fostered, the inner spirit can remain very much alive. Trusting in the truth which our own heart dictates, we continue to learn. As the Book of Wisdom reminds us: 'In the secret of my heart teach me wisdom.'

Hope

Ageing in hope can be summed up well in the words of the four-
teenth century English mystic, Julian of Norwich: 'All shall be
well, and all shall be well, and you shall perceive how all manner of things shall be well.' Hope is rooted in reality and so it is
not to be associated with mere fantasy or an unreal sense of optimism. Neither is hope realised in the mere fulfilment of wishes.
It is something deeper and more open-ended. Hope provides an
outlook which trusts in the possibilities that are open to those
who endeavour to live their human existence to the full.
Disappointments will occur, but hope does not allow these to
take hold. In fact it is often through coping with disappointments that a hopeful person discovers the possibility of new
openings and wider horizons opening up to them. Hope chal-
lenges to what lies further, to what is beyond our normal range
of inner vision. It stretches us to both the beyond as well as to the
greater depths that exist in the present. There is always more to
each moment than we have the capacity to experience, but
growth in hope liberates us to develop further our potential to a
far wider and deeper range of experiences. Hope is closely
linked with courage and an explorer spirit.

An essential dimension of hope is that it does not allow a sense
of ultimate disappointment or hopelessness to permeate the
inner core of our being. True hope, too, helps to ease away the
pain of remorse, bitterness and regret. While hope admits these
and other negative feelings, hope has the power to filter through
and allow new vistas to open up, particularly as we start to let
go of that which is diminishing us. Hope also allows for a
change in priorities to take place, where what is experienced as
personally enriching, rather than the 'oughts' in life, takes
greater precedence. It is never too late 'to fall in love with life', as
Shirley Valentine so well articulated.

Hope is very much connected with vision – a vision which includes within it the notion 'that the best is still to come'. When
we no longer cling to our illusions, vision, perspective and insight flourish. Hope is closely linked with enlightenment which
is connected with these latter three qualities. Illumination leads

to changed meanings, changed perspectives, even to a changed notion about time. Hope is about letting go of anxiety, and especially excessive anxiety regarding the future, while at the same time it does not avoid planning in a reasonable manner for the years ahead.

Even the experience of darkness, fatigue, or depression does not quench hope, or at least need not. Living with the knowledge that things pass and that the power of hope is there to sustain us in such circumstances gives, even if only dimly, the ability to live with the expectancy of something greater to come. Darkness can overwhelm us, particularly if we shut out the many signs of light which both surround us and lie deep within ourselves. The darkness of the older years found in much thinking and literature on ageing (including the discussions on euthanasia) is partly due to a failure to see the light that is available to all who wish to discover it in the 'now' opportunities of our individual life situations.

Hope is a gift, a quality which emerges from the actual living of life. It is often linked with endurance, the ability to hang in, even when the going is difficult. But when we can do this, as St Paul reminds us, 'hope does not disappoint us'. Those with religious faith and those who profess none are blessed if they remain open to the future, aware that life has always something more, something new to offer us. Someone who lives with hope will not find life dull, drab or boring. Each day offers fresh opportunities, fresh surprises. Mostly these will not be dramatic, but are there to be savoured in all their simplicity and ordinariness. A Taoist story is revealing and may be helpful to those who may experience some difficulty in identifying with what has been written about hope:

> 'The carpenter said to his apprentice: "Do you know why this tree is so big and so old?" The apprentice said "No. Why?" Then the carpenter answered: "Because it is useless. If it were useful it would have been cut down, sawn up and used for beds and tables and chairs. But because it is useless, it has been allowed to grow. That is why it is now so great that you can rest in its shadow."'

When we grow to accept ourselves for who we are, and not link our value to past achievements or what we can or cannot do in the now, then we, like the tree, reach maturity. The power of hope which allows us to trust in ourselves and others is what brings life. The expanding visions which grow through hope, even as the ageing process takes its toll, enables us to see beyond limitations. It invites us to surrender to life as it is now, and it is where 'the distinction between life and death loses its pain.' (H. Nouwen.)

Hope is linked with desires. We have surface desires which are not always in tune with the truth of who we are. Discernment is needed to discover our deep down desires, some of which may need to be enlivened by hope to come to fulfilment. Desires and dreams are related to one another, and unfulfilled dreams of earlier years can sometimes find realisation in unexpected ways, if opportunities are explored and connections made between the dream and our real world. Hope too gives the courage which allows us to earth our dreams. All this becomes possible if we listen to what our dreams are saying to us. Allowing the attempts of others to dampen, diminish or even laugh at our hopes and dreams must be fought. Pope John XXIII is an outstanding example of an older person who allowed his dream about a Church Council to take root. This particular dream has affected the lives of many people and has even shaped history in a remarkable way.

Our attitude to death, our own in particular, will colour the level of hope experienced. Some people have a natural fear of death, although such a fear is often more about the process of dying rather than death itself. Fear is an emotion largely connected with the unknown, and death is the great unknown. Religious faith may help some people to alleviate this fear, but faith of itself does not guarantee the elimination of the fear of death. It is important that the presence or absence of fear be not taken as a measure of a person's faith, either by themselves or by others. Fear of death, like other forms of fear, has to be gently faced and worked through, and this may require the help of another person if its crippling effect is to be lessened. Erik Ericson remarked 'that only in a society in which the old do not fear death, will the young be able not to fear life. Put another way, it could be stated that only in a society in which the old find meaning in their lives, will the young have confidence in any meanings they may be offered.'

Aldous Huxley gives great hope when he says to his dying wife: 'Let go, let go … go forward into the light. Let yourself be carried into the light. No memories, no regrets, no looking backwards, no apprehensive thoughts about your own or anyone else's future. Only light.' These words are echoed in similar fashion by a dying Dutch priest, Han Fortman: 'I proceed from the simple irrefutable fact that in the crucial moments of life (such as death), even though people come from diverging cultures and religions, they find that same essential word: Light! For isn't it true? There must be a basic similarity between the Enlightenment spoken of by the Hindus and Buddhists and the Eternal Light of the Christians. Both die into the Light.'

Light, enlightenment, is not only for those approaching death. It is a reality that can be progressively discovered in the ordinary things of our everyday, as well as in the extraordinary moments. Enlightenment is a fruit of hope which enables us to remain open to all that happens to us, and particularly as we continue our exploring work of completing both our outer and inner life's journey. T.S. Eliot explains this sentiment so well when he says: 'Old men ought to be explorers, here or there does not matter. To a further intensity, a deeper communion …. In the end is our beginning.'

Joy

One of the best ways of opening people to profound human truths is through the power of a story and this particular section will both begin and end with one.

> 'The Master was in an expansive mood so his disciples sought to learn from him the stages he had passed through in his quest for the divine. "God first led me by the hand," he said, "into the Land of Action and there I dwelt for several years. Then he returned and led me to the Land of Sorrows; there I lived until my heart was

purged of every inordinate attachment. That is when I found myself in the Land of Love whose burning flames consumed whatever was left in me of self. This brought me to the Land of Silence where the mysteries of life and death were bared before my wondering eyes." "Was that the final stage of your quest?" they asked. "No," the Master said. "One day God said, 'Today I shall take you to the innermost sanctuary of the Temple, to the heart of God himself.' And I was led to the Land of Laughter."'

Joy is one of our primary emotions and is associated with a range of feeling experiences, from moments of ecstasy, passion, exhilaration, to a quieter form of inner contentment. Feelings of joy can surge up at unexpected moments, or joy can be the normal inner state that pervades the life of an individual. Joy can manifest itself in various outward expressions, from smiles and laughter to dancing and even jumping for joy. Joy is mentioned several times in the Bible: 'However great the number of years a man may live, let him enjoy them all. No enjoyment surpasses a cheerful heart. Joy is what gives him length of days.' (Book of Wisdom) At the heart of the gospel is the theme of joy, this central message being announced at the outset: 'I bring you news of great joy,' to which is added immediately, 'a joy to be shared by the whole people'.

Much discussion on ageing focuses on its difficulties, and little is said about its joys. It is something like the way bad news makes the headlines, while good news rarely does. Stereotyping ageing, especially seeing the older years in the light of the 17% of people who are frail and dependant, highlights the unattractive face of ageing in society's consciousness. While deep joy can and does exist in the lives of these 17% of people, it is abundantly open to the remaining 83% to experience much joy as they age.

Unlike wisdom, which can be sought, or hope, whose presence can be encouraged and fostered, joy is something that happens to us. We cannot seek it, in fact the more we consciously try to do so, the more it eludes us. It is a by-product of our attitudes and desires and the way we live our lives. Joy is more likely to emerge if we value life and notice its preciousness in both the small and major happenings of ordinary everyday living, such as the smile of a baby, an unexpected meeting, a beauty of nature, an insight received. Joy in other words is about delighting in, wondering at, being playful about all that happens in the world around us, and what takes place within ourselves. Everything, even the tragic moments, can in some way have a joy-filled dimension. One of the great joyous moments is undoubtedly for a mother at the birth of her child. She forgets the pain when the baby is born. Yet why is it that joy seems to evaporate, appear almost non-existent in the lives of many? Experiencing life as fulfilling must surely be connected with recapturing and discovering in new ways the joy dimension of living. It is available to all of us.

Joy is something which invades us – all we can do is pre-dispose ourselves for it. Like falling asleep or falling in love, so too we fall into joy. Joy is more likely to come to those who try to live liberated lives; to those who consciously work at developing inner freedom; to those who try to get rid of the clutter that accumulates over life, both from within and without. Such a freedom is sensitive to the freedom of others, while it attempts to eliminate the barriers that restrict our own lack of freedom. Living joyfully in this sense entails the letting go of many things, some of which may be very precious. Ultimately it includes the letting go of our own life. Sometimes even death, the death of a joy-filled person, can exude an atmosphere of joy which reaches out and touches those present. Death is the great mysterious event. As a small child, Claim Potok recalls asking his father why a bird should die, why death at all, and received the following answer: 'So life would be precious. Something that is yours forever is never precious.' Growth in awareness of the fragility of all that is, of the transient nature of everything, greatly assists us in appreciating joyous moments as they come to us. Moments of intense joy, even rapture can last for mere seconds, but the remembrance of them can remain a lifetime.

Joy is linked with humour, which has been described as knowledge with a soft smile. Humour's knowledge is a great blessing to possess. Humour has the capacity to relativise without ridiculing or becoming cynical. It enables us to take ourselves, others and life events seriously, but never too seriously. To be able to see the humorous side of things is all part of growth in understanding and thus is a valued way of coming closer to truth. So much in human living is relative - values, issues, people, even life itself. A great realisation that comes gradually over life is that nothing is absolute except love. 'Love never ends' says a famous biblical phrase. In relation to love, everything else fades into insignificance.

A humorous person has the ability to discover fun almost any-where. Such people are often very balanced since they have a healthy perspective on life and generally they are good to be with. Humour and joy are often connected with playfulness, an activity so prominent and essential in the life of a child. Play leads to delight and often wonder, both of which result in joy. Play is not the same as a leisure activity. The latter can often be very serious and demanding. Play is spontaneous, refreshes, is an experience of fun and freedom and often has an outside-time quality about it. The laughter and smiles of children, especially at play, have an appealing, contagious quality. The laughter and smiles of older people can also be special. The joy that is found in younger and older people often carries a particular type of ra-diance so that their joy affects not only themselves but reaches out to touch others in a special way. Laughter, joy and play all help the serious world we live in to become more light-hearted. A heavy-hearted person has great difficulty in experiencing joy in living. Groucho Marx was someone who brought a sense of fun and lightheartedness to many people by his playful pranks on film. He seems also to have experienced joy himself: 'Each morning when I open my eyes I say to myself; "I, not events, have the power to make me happy or unhappy today. I can chose which it shall be. Yesterday is dead, tomorrow hasn't ar-rived yet. I have just one day, today, and I'm going to be happy in it."'

Joy can be something bubbly or it can manifest itself in serenity and contentment. This latter state of living is likely to be the con-sequence of our approach to life, which does not allow circum-stances and events, even if traumatic, to upset us unduly. Upset clouds perception and only adds to the trauma. Fortunately, we

now live in an age where medicine, in particular good drug ther-
apy and other helps, can eliminate or keep to a minimum physical pain. The causes of emotional and spiritual pain come from
ourselves since both types of suffering arise from our personal
reactions to the circumstances of our lives. The chapter on stress
discussed how to develop our ability to cope with such suffering.

Someone who knows the world of joy is more likely to be earthed in the real world and live in the present. Even if that present
proves difficult, it is rarely intolerable. No event, no matter how
extreme the pain that surrounds it, has the power to take away
our joy unless we allow it to do so. Each happening in life is
open to being joy-filled at a deep level, and responsible living is
about not being pulled down by upset feelings, which often are
surface and will pass, especially if we manage them constructively. Dietrich Bonhoeffer writes movingly from prison in his
last letter to his fiancee just before his execution: 'I have not felt
lonely or abandoned for one moment. You must not think that I
am unhappy. What is happiness and what is unhappiness? It depends so little on the circumstances. It depends really on that
which happens inside a person. I am grateful every day that I
have you, and that makes me happy.'

Anthony de Mello calls us 'to wake up' to life, to 're-discover
life'. Certainly this is the path to follow if we wish to experience
our older years as fulfilling. We cannot acquire joy, as he points
out, since we already have it. What happens is that we block it
from surfacing in our lives. Hence our task is to remove the
blocks and allow joy's existence to flourish. He quotes an eastern
saying: 'When the eye is unobstructed, the result is sight; when
the mind is unobstructed, the result is truth; when the heart is
unobstructed, the result is joy and love.' What we tend to see
and name as our sources of joy can often be the very things that
bind us and thus hinder us from experiencing true joy. For example, if our hearts are too attached to wealth, possessions, relationships, health, or our 'enjoyments', such things can result in
our lack of joy. Fear of losing, or actual loss of these possessions
can take hold of us and actually prevent real joy surfacing. If actual loss does occur, a sense of devastation can ensue. There is so
much in life that can give joy, but if we over-focus on particular

people, places, possessions as the source of our joy, and then one of these is no longer there for us, or is not there in the way we would like it to be there, then we can become sad, upset, frustrated and lacking in joy. Another eastern quotation aptly says: 'When you enjoy the scent of a thousand flowers, you are not going to feel too bad at the lack of one.' In other words, our joy does not depend on any one person or thing - Mary or George, our possessions, ideas, talents or good health. Our heart is inevitably drawn to where our treasure is. If our treasure lies solely in people and/or possessions, it will be tied there. If our treasure is in freedom, love, beauty, truth, then the heart which is tied to these has an endless source of joy available in the world around us. This does not mean that we do not have possessions or value our relationships, but it does mean that they are not our sole treasures in life.

It is very difficult to define joy for ourselves, and one of the reasons is that it is hard to experience true joy until we begin to drop our attachments. Everyone recognises moments of joy when they happen, and such moments tend to have a fleeting quality about them. A particular characteristic of joyous moments is that they are unexpected, unique, carry their own special flavour, and are largely unrepeatable. Joy is not to be confused with thrills or pleasure. Joy is something which deeply satisfies the human heart, since it is something which affects the core of our spirit. In its most profound sense, joy is about the experience of bliss. Such an experience is open to each one and a step in the direction of tasting such an experience is to believe in its possibility.

As we grow in freedom and unattachment, we are left with more energy and enthusiasm for living. We are also likely to become more empowering and creative as people. Allowing ourselves to be surprised by the happenings of our personal lives is a way to facilitate the emergence of joy. C.S. Lewis titled his autobiography 'Surprised by joy'. Soon after it was finished, he was entirely surprised by one of the greatest joys of his life – Joy in person and in name, who became his wife!

This section will end with another eastern story, entitled *The*

Diamond, which illustrates well a source where true and abundant joy is found:

The wise man had reached the outskirts of the village and settled down under a tree for the night, when a villager came running up to him and said, 'The stone! The stone! Give me the precious stone.' 'What stone?' asked the wise man. 'Last night the Lord Shiva appeared to me in a dream,' said the villager, 'and told me that if I went to the outskirts of the village at dusk I should find a wise man who would give me a precious stone that would make me rich forever.' The wise man rummaged in his bag and pulled out a stone. 'He probably meant this one,' he said, as he handed the stone over to the villager. 'I found it in a forest path some days ago. You can certainly have it.' The man gazed at the stone in wonder. It was a diamond, probably the largest diamond in the whole world, for it was as large as a person's head. He took the diamond and walked away. All night he tossed about in bed, unable to sleep. Next day at the crack of dawn he woke the wise man and said, 'Give me the wealth that makes it possible for you to give this diamond away so easily.'

In conclusion

'Length of days is not what makes age honourable
nor number of years the true measure of life.
Understanding, this is man's grey hairs.'
(Book of Wisdom)

This book has been about falling in love with life, living life to
the full, which is achieved through greater understanding,
especially understanding the ageing process, as we live our lives
from the fifties on. Any new understanding that has been gained
will hopefully open the reader to see the years ahead as a time of
endless possibilities for personal enrichment and fulfilment. If
the door has been opened a bit further to enable even a few to
face the challenge of living life with greater zest and hope, it will
have been worthwhile.

By the same author

Who Cares?

A GUIDE FOR ALL WHO CARE FOR OTHERS

Catherine McCann

The word 'carer' is a fairly recent coinage, but many of us are involved one way or another in caring for others – family carers, parents, health and social workers, teachers, etc. – and the importance of quality care in the lives of many people is increasingly recognised.

In*Who Cares?* Catherine McCann asks who are the carers and how do they care? What can be done to improve and enhance the care that they give? She believes that compassion, and the relationship between carer and cared-for, are at the heart of successful caring. She combines her considerable professional experience with a deep personal compassion, to offer advice, inspiration, consolation and encouragement to all who care.

There is a comprehensive appendix of organisations and support groups, with addresses and phone numbers, which all carers will find invaluable.

'Anybody who reads this book will learn a startling amount from it. It is the kind of book that can change people's lives.'
— Brendan Kennelly from the Forword

ISBN 1 85607 126 X   136pp £5.99

the columba press